MODERN CONCEPTS IN CHEMISTRY

EDITORS

Bryce Crawford, Jr., University of Minnesota
W. D. McElroy, Johns Hopkins University
Charles C. Price, University of Pennsylvania

C. G. OVERBERGER, Ph.D., University of Illinois, is Dean of Science, Director of the Polymer Research Institute, and Professor of Organic Chemistry at the Polytechnic Institute of Brooklyn. Dr. Overberger is a member of the Board of Directors and President (1967) of the American Chemical Society and Editor of the *Journal of Polymer Science* and the *Advances in Polymer Science* series. He has been active in many areas of research, including decomposition of azo compounds, linear and cyclic; elimination reactions of diazenes; ionic polymerization and polymer synthesis.

J-P. ANSELME, Ph.D., Polytechnic Institute of Brooklyn, is Assistant Professor of Chemistry at the University of Massachusetts, Boston. Formerly a Research Associate and Senior Instructor at the Polytechnic Institute of Brooklyn, Dr. Anselme is a member of several professional societies, including the American Chemical Society, The Chemical Society of London, the Gesellschaft Deutscher Chemiker, and the Chemical Society of Japan. His major research interests are nitrogen compounds and non-benzenoid aromatic heterocycles.

J. G. LOMBARDINO, Ph.D., Polytechnic Institute of Brooklyn, is a Research Chemist with Chas. Pfizer & Co., Inc. A member of the American Chemical Society and the American Institute of Chemists, Dr. Lombardino's fields of· interest include synthetic organic medicinals and nitrogen heterocycles.

ORGANIC COMPOUNDS
WITH
NITROGEN-NITROGEN BONDS

C. G. OVERBERGER
POLYTECHNIC INSTITUTE OF BROOKLYN

J-P. ANSELME
UNIVERSITY OF MASSACHUSETTS, BOSTON

J. G. LOMBARDINO
CHAS. PFIZER & CO., INC.

THE RONALD PRESS COMPANY • NEW YORK

Preface

When we were initially approached about writing on the chemistry of azo and diazo compounds, it was quite clear to us that an all-inclusive volume involved a monumental task and was impractical because of the amount of time available. Accordingly, we have prepared a short monograph covering topics in which we have a personal interest, including areas where we have contributed to the original literature and in which we wish to express our opinion.

We have relied heavily on previous books on the chemistry of nitrogen compounds, in particular the outstanding book by Zollinger, *Azo and Diazo Chemistry, Aliphatic and Aromatic Compounds*. We have correlated and interpreted information in eight general categories as indicated by the chapter headings. An attempt has been made to cover as much of the recent literature as possible. We have omitted the work of many excellent investigators or simply stated in a very cursory way some facts with an appropriate reference to subjects which may be of vital interest to many but are not germane to the development of our point of view.

It is of interest to reflect on the rapid development of certain aspects of the chemistry of azo and diazo compounds—many of which are covered in this brief review. The classical interest in azo compounds was derived primarily from the early work on aromatic azo dyes and diazo compounds of the aromatic type as well as the chemistry of heterocyclics which contain vicinal nitrogen atoms.

The new developments in cyclic azo compounds have largely been those of a non-aromatic character, although there is considerable interest in compounds of the latter type as well, in structures other than the conventional 5- and 6-membered rings. The recognition of the existence of 3-membered rings containing the nitrogen-nitrogen double bond has stimulated intense interest in the stereochemistry of the azo linkage.

Although the concept of the nitrogen sextet in classical rearrangements of the Hoffman and Curtius types has been of interest for many years, the chemistry of nitrogen sextets has certainly "mushroomed" over the past ten years, and we emphasize this point. The types of "diazo-like" intermediates derived from hydrazines that contain this nitrogen sextet have occupied an important part of our research effort. We have attempted to reflect the use of the newer physical methods such as infrared, nuclear magnetic resonance, and electron spin resonance, which have had a major effect on the development of the chemistry of azo and diazo compounds.

Our special thanks go to Mr. Ned Weinshenker, who helped proofread the final drafts, to Marie-Céline Anselme for her help in preparing the Index, and to Dr. William Daly for his personal assistance.

C. G. OVERBERGER
J-P. ANSELME
J. G. LOMBARDINO

Contents

ORGANIC COMPOUNDS
WITH
NITROGEN-NITROGEN BONDS

I

Introduction

1-1. REACTIVITY OF COMPOUNDS WITH NITROGEN-NITROGEN BONDS

A discussion of the reactivity and stability of the nitrogen-nitrogen bond must necessarily involve comparison with other common atomic bonds. In Table 1–1 are listed the experimental values[1]* of the dissociation energies of the bonds to be discussed.

TABLE I–I
Dissociation Energies of Bonds

Bond	Energy (kcal./mole)	Bond	Energy (kcal./mole)	Bond	Energy (kcal./mole)
N—N	37	N=N	61 [2]	N≡N	225 [2]
C—C	80	C=C	145	C≡C	198
C—N	66	C=N	112 [3]	C≡N	209
S—S	64	O=O	96		

An inspection of Table 1–1 reveals an important fact about the nitrogen-nitrogen system: the saturated nitrogen system (N—N) has the *lowest* dissociation energy among the common bonds; in contrast, the system containing the most multiple links between nitrogen atoms (N≡N) has the *highest* dissociation energy. This abnormally high stability for the N≡N system, making elemental nitrogen the most stable diatomic molecule known, will help to explain many of the reactions of the nitrogen-nitrogen bond to be discussed in later chapters.

Since two nitrogen atoms may be joined by either a single, a double, or a triple bond, the following discussion will treat each group separately.

1-2. SATURATED NITROGEN-NITROGEN BONDS

Reactions of the saturated nitrogen-nitrogen bond with oxidizing or reducing agents will very often proceed in one of two ways: either the weak

* Numbered references in the text are listed at the end of the chapter.

nitrogen-nitrogen bond will be reductively cleaved to the corresponding amines or the compound will be oxidized to some intermediate which, given sufficient energy, will dissociate to evolve elemental nitrogen.   Examples of reductive cleavage are

$$RC{-}NHNH_2 + H_2 \xrightarrow{Ni} RC{-}NH_2 + NH_3 \qquad (1\text{--}1)$$
$$\underset{O}{\overset{\|}{}} \qquad\qquad\qquad \underset{O}{\overset{\|}{}}$$

$$Ar{-}\underset{\underset{NO}{|}}{N}{-}Ar + Na_2S_2O_4 \longrightarrow Ar{-}\underset{\underset{H}{|}}{N}{-}Ar \qquad (1\text{--}2)$$

As shown in Table 1–1, the energy required to cleave the nitrogen-nitrogen bond is much lower than that needed to cleave a carbon-carbon bond.   As a result, the reactions illustrated (1–1 and 1–2) are carried out at 80°C or lower, far below the elevated temperatures normally required to cleave the carbon-carbon bond in hydrocarbons. As with all types of bonds, the strength of a particular nitrogen-nitrogen bond will vary with the substituents on the atoms involved.   Values as low as 13 kcal./mole for the nitrogen-nitrogen bond in $O_2N{-}NO_2$ and 10 kcal./mole in $O_2N{-}NO$ have been reported.[4]   In these cases, both steric and electronegative forces due to the oxygen atoms serve to weaken the nitrogen-nitrogen bond further.

When a saturated nitrogen-nitrogen bond is oxidized, the product is often nitrogen or some intermediate compound which can be made to evolve nitrogen if sufficient energy is supplied.   Some examples to illustrate this point are

$$RNHNHR \xrightarrow{[O]} R{-}N{=}N{-}R \xrightarrow{\Delta} R{-}R + N_2 + RH \qquad (1\text{--}3)$$

$$R_2N{-}NH_2 \xrightarrow{[O]} R_2N{-}N{=}N{-}NR_2 \xrightarrow{\Delta}$$
$$N_2 + \text{nitrogen-containing compounds} \quad (1\text{--}4)$$

$$Ar{-}\underset{\underset{N}{\|}}{C}{-}\underset{\underset{N}{\|}}{C}{-}Ar \xrightarrow{[O]} ArC{\equiv}CAr + 2\,N_2 \qquad (1\text{--}5)$$
$$\underset{H_2N}{\diagup} \qquad \underset{NH_2}{\diagdown}$$

$$ArCH_2{-}\underset{\underset{NH_2}{|}}{N}{-}CH_2Ar \xrightarrow{[O]} ArCH_2CH_2Ar + N_2 \qquad (1\text{--}6)$$

The intermediate products of reactions (1–3) and (1–4) can sometimes be isolated, whereas reactions (1–5) and (1–6) proceed directly to give elemental nitrogen and the indicated products. The intermediates of reactions (1–3) and (1–4) (called azo compounds and tetrazenes, respectively) will be discussed in later chapters.

1–3. UNSATURATED NITROGEN-NITROGEN BONDS

An unsaturated link in a chain of *carbon* atoms is usually the reactive site in the molecule. Almost all reactions carried out on olefinic and acetylenic derivatives will take place at the point of unsaturation, while the more vigorous reactions will actually cleave these compounds at the unsaturated bond:

$$R\text{—}CH\text{=}CH\text{—}R + KMnO_4 \xrightarrow{\Delta} 2\ RCOOH \qquad (1\text{–}7)$$

In a compound containing an unsaturated nitrogen-nitrogen bond (N=N) however, the bond between the nitrogen atoms never cleaves during a reaction, but rather the tendency is for the —N=N— portion of the molecule to separate as nitrogen. This phenomenon can best be observed in the azides (1–8), tetrazenes (1–4), azo and diazo compounds (1–9) to be discussed separately in later chapters:

$$RCON_3 + H_2O \xrightarrow{Ag^+} N_2 + RNH_2 + CO_2 \qquad (1\text{–}8)$$

$$RCHN_2 + HX \longrightarrow N_2 + RCH_2X \qquad (1\text{–}9)$$

As has previously been noted, the driving force for the formation of the very stable elemental nitrogen is a strong one.[1] Conversion of a saturated nitrogen-nitrogen bond (e.g. a hydrazine) to elemental nitrogen, i.e.

$$\underset{(a)}{\diagdown N\text{—}N \diagup} \rightarrow \underset{(b)}{\text{—}N\text{=}N\text{—}} \rightarrow \underset{(c)}{N\text{≡}N}$$

is a very favorable sequence from the standpoint of energy changes. Pitzer[1] has pointed out that a *repulsive* force exists between the P orbitals of the *saturated* nitrogen system (a), thus making the N—N bond longer (1.40 Å) than the sum of the atomic radii of two nitrogen atoms (0.53 Å). The P orbitals in elemental nitrogen (c), however, have *attractive* forces between them which further stabilize the bonding between the atoms. Consequently, chemical reactions performed on the hydrazine (a) which produce nitrogen (c) will proceed readily. This great stability of elemental nitrogen, then, exerts a profound effect on the course of a reaction involving a nitrogen-nitrogen bond. Since it is a product of such low energy (i.e. high stability), the production of nitrogen in a reaction almost always gives rise to a net *decrease* in the free energy content of the reaction system. The accompanying figure graphically depicts the change in free energy in the transformation of starting materials (A) to products (B).

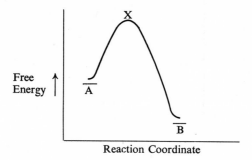

A difference in energy between A (the free energy of starting material) and B (the free energy of product) is always an important factor in determining whether any reaction is theoretically possible. When B is of lower energy than A, as shown in the figure, the reaction will be theoretically possible, although no statements as to reaction conditions or kinetics can be made. When the product (B) is at an exceptionally low energy level, as is the case when elemental nitrogen is formed, the reaction then has a stronger driving force. In transforming a molecule of energy A to a product of energy B, a net change in free energy (A minus B) takes place which makes energy available for raising still other molecules of starting material over the barrier of the transition state (X in the figure). Thus the conversion of a system containing a saturated nitrogen-nitrogen bond to elemental nitrogen not only produces a stable, low-energy product, but at the same time provides some of the energy for promoting the conversion of still other molecules of starting material to products. It should further be pointed out that the compounds which serve as precursors of nitrogen gas, such as azo and diazo compounds, diazonium salts, and azides, are of comparatively high energy, thus making the starting point A higher on the graph and making the net decrease in free energy (A minus B) greater than that found for most reactions.

Finally, it is important to note that nitrogen gas, once formed in a reaction, leaves the site of reaction. Thus, *no equilibria are possible* in a reaction that produces elemental nitrogen and, whenever possible, the starting material will be *totally* converted to products.

A comparison of the reactions of the three unsaturated bonds $\diagdown$C$=$C$\diagup$, $\diagdown$C$=$N$-$, and $-$N$=$N$-$ points up the greater electronegativity of the nitrogen atom as compared to the carbon atom. In the carbon-nitrogen double bond $\left(\diagdown \text{C}=\text{N}- \right)$ the polarization of the bond toward the nitrogen atom permits facile addition of nucleophilic agents to the carbon atom:

$$\text{C}{=}\text{N}{-} + \text{HB:} \rightarrow \left[\overset{+}{\text{HB}}{-}\text{C}{-}\overset{-}{\text{N}}{-} \right] \rightarrow \text{B}{-}\text{C}{-}\text{NH}{-} \qquad (1\text{--}10)$$

For example, organometallic reagents have been added to both aliphatic and aromatic carbon-nitrogen double bonds (e.g. pyridine). Comparison of the carbon-nitrogen double bond $\left(\text{C}{=}\text{N}{-} \right)$ with the isolated carbon-carbon double bond $\left(\text{C}{=}\text{C} \right)$ indicates an increased reactivity of the former bond toward a variety of nucleophiles and to reducing agents. A variety of metal hydrides useful in reducing $\left(\text{C}{=}\text{N}{-} \right)$ bonds do not reduce the $\left(\text{C}{=}\text{C} \right)$ bond, again illustrating the more polar nature of the former.

Additions across the nitrogen-nitrogen double bond ($-\text{N}{=}\text{N}-$) are well known. A particularly well-studied system is the addition of nucleophiles to azodicarboxylic ester; additions to this $\text{N}{=}\text{N}$ bond proceed exothermally at room temperature.

Doubly unsaturated bonds of the carbon and nitrogen systems ($\text{C}{\equiv}\text{C}$, $\text{C}{=}\text{N}$, $\text{N}{\equiv}\text{N}$) show extraordinary differences in their reactivities. The acetylenic system ($\text{C}{\equiv}\text{C}$) exhibits a high reactivity in oxidations (often explosively), in reductions, and in some addition reactions. For example, hydration of acetylene provides a commercial process for the preparation of acetaldehyde, while reactions with halo acids provide a convenient source of vinyl monomers:

$$\text{HC}{\equiv}\text{CH} + \text{HX} \rightarrow \text{CH}_2{=}\text{CHX} \qquad (1\text{--}11)$$

Nitrile groups, ($\text{C}{\equiv}\text{N}$), exhibit many of the properties found in reactions of the $\left(\text{C}{=}\text{N}{-} \right)$ function previously discussed. These properties are again due to the polarization of the bond toward the nitrogen atom. Hydrolysis of nitriles to amides, reductions to amines, and conversion to imino ethers are but a few examples of some of the common reactions performed on the polar nitrile function.

Acetylenic links are, as might be expected, less stable and *more* reactive than their saturated or doubly bonded precursors. Elemental nitrogen, however, is unique in having an unsaturated bond together with high stability. It is inert to all common reagents and far *less* reactive than its saturated (e.g. hydrazine) or doubly bonded (e.g. azo compounds) precursors. In fact, nitrogen gas is often used as an inert atmosphere in many reactions. No common oxidation or reduction systems available in the laboratory will affect elemental nitrogen.   Commercially, however, the ready availability of nitrogen from fractionation of liquid air (nitrogen comprising 78% of air by volume) has made practical some processes under extreme conditions of temperature and pressure.   For example, the Haber process for reducing nitrogen with hydrogen to produce ammonia requires 1000 atmospheres of pressure and a temperature of 600°C.   Oxidation of nitrogen by oxygen to produce nitric oxide required an electric arc to attain a reaction temperature of 2000°C.   This latter process, as duplicated in the atmosphere by lightning, forms the various oxides of nitrogen, which are then brought to earth by rain, eventually to become valuable constituents of plants and animals.   Another reaction of elemental nitrogen, again using very high temperatures, is the combination with various metals such as lithium, magnesium, calcium, and boron to form the respective nitrides.

To summarize then, the high reactivity of both the saturated and doubly bonded nitrogen-nitrogen bond is due to (1) the weak bond joining saturated nitrogen atoms and (2) the great stability of the elemental nitrogen which is a product of most reactions of nitrogen-nitrogen bonds.

REFERENCES

General

N. SIDGWICK, *The Organic Chemistry of Nitrogen*, Clarendon Press, London, 1937.

Text

1. K. S. PITZER, *J. Am. Chem. Soc.*, **70**, 2140 (1948).
2. N. SIDGWICK, *The Organic Chemistry of Nitrogen*, Clarendon Press, London, 1937.
3. L. FIESER and M. FIESER, *Organic Chemistry*, 3d ed., Reinhold Publishing Corp., New York, 1956, p. 1111.
4. T. L. COTTRELL, *The Strength of Chemical Bonds*, Butterworth & Co. Ltd., London, 1951.

2

Hydrazine and Its Derivatives

2-1. INTRODUCTION; GENERALITIES

Since a great many organic compounds contain two linked nitrogen atoms, it might be best to begin by discussing those compounds containing bonded nitrogen atoms in their lowest oxidation states. First to be considered in this category is the parent compound, hydrazine (I):

$$
\begin{array}{ccc}
H & & H \\
\diagdown & & \diagup \\
& N{-}N & \\
\diagup & & \diagdown \\
H & & H \\
& I &
\end{array}
$$

The increasing interest[1a,b] in hydrazine and its derivatives is due partly to military uses for certain hydrazines as rocket propellants and also to the varied medicinal uses[1c] found for hydrazine derivatives. Hydrazine is a highly reactive compound; oxidation can occur on mere exposure to air, proceeding through a diimide intermediate (*vide infra*) to yield nitrogen. As the discussion in a previous chapter indicated, conversion of hydrazine to elemental nitrogen produces a great amount of energy. For this reason, and because of the ready availability of hydrazine from ammonia by the Raschig process, i.e.

$$2\,NH_3 + NaOCl \rightarrow NH_2NH_2 + NaCl + H_2O \qquad (2\text{--}1)$$

hydrazine has found wide use as a rocket fuel. Used in conjunction with nitric acid as the oxidizing agent, the gaseous products of hydrazine oxidation (e.g. nitrogen, oxides of nitrogen) produce very efficient thrust. Some of the disadvantages of hydrazine as a fuel include its low stability in air and its corrosive properties, making it difficult to handle and store. Tetrafluorohydrazine has been prepared from nitrogen trifluoride at elevated temperatures but, as expected, the presence of the highly electronegative fluorine atoms makes this compound even less stable than hydrazine. Methylhydrazine, with its somewhat more favorable physical properties, appears to be replacing hydrazine as a liquid rocket fuel.

9

Preparative methods for the various substituted hydrazines have been described[2,3,4] in several texts and will not be reviewed here, while more recent reviews[5] survey some newer methods for preparing hydrazines. Generally, hydrazine derivatives may be divided into the mono-, di-, tri-, and tetrasubstituted hydrazines; disubstituted hydrazines may be further subdivided into the 1,1- or 1,2-substituted hydrazines:

$$R-NH-NH_2 \qquad \text{(a)} \quad RNH-NHR \qquad \overset{R}{\underset{R}{\diagup}}N-NH-R \qquad \overset{R}{\underset{R}{\diagup}}N-N\overset{R}{\underset{R}{\diagup}}$$

(mono-)   (tri-)   (tetra-)

$$\text{(b)} \quad \overset{R}{\underset{R}{\diagup}}N-NH_2$$

(di-)

II   III   IV   V

Monosubstituted hydrazines (II) are chemically similar to the unsubstituted parent compound I and, as such, are readily oxidized by a variety of oxidizing agents including air. Other oxidizing agents react readily with monosubstituted hydrazines; thus, bromine oxidizes phenylhydrazine to bromobenzene and nitrogen. Alkylation of monosubstituted hydrazines yields 1,1-dialkylhydrazines as well as more highly substituted hydrazines. Phenylhydrazine, although claimed by many to be methylated (by methyl iodide) on the 2-nitrogen atom to give 1-phenyl-2-methylhydrazine, has been reported by at least three workers to alkylate at the 1-nitrogen atom (2–2). Consideration should be given to the possible transition states in an alkylation of a substituted hydrazine. A developing positive charge will best be stabilized by a substituted nitrogen atom; the intermediate shown in Equation (2–2) can be stabilized through inductive effects of the aromatic ring, whereas the alternative 1,2-disubstituted intermediate cannot:

$$\phi NHNH_2 + CH_3I \rightarrow \left[\overset{\phi}{\underset{CH_3}{\diagup}}\overset{+}{N}H-NH_2I^- \right] \rightarrow \overset{\phi}{\underset{CH_3}{\diagup}}N-NH_2 + HI \quad (2\text{–}2)$$

$$CH_3NHNH_2 + CH_3I \rightarrow (CH_3)_2N-NH_2 + HI \quad (2\text{–}3)$$

Monosubstituted hydrazines react with carbonyl compounds of various kinds. When reacted with aldehydes or ketones, the products are hydrazones (see Chapter 3) and water. With carboxylic acids, acid halides, or esters, 1-substituted hydrazines react to form hydrazides (see Chapter 6). Of the many hydrazines of type II, phenylhydrazine has found use in sugar chemistry (i.e. formation of osazones), while 2,4-dinitrophenylhydrazine is widely used in identifying aldehydes and ketones as their solid dinitrophenylhydrazones.

Disubstituted hydrazines (III) must be subdivided, and the two classes considered separately, since the presence of the primary amine function in the 1,1-disubstituted hydrazines (IIIb) allows very different reaction properties from those of the 1,2-disubstituted hydrazines (IIIa).

2–2.   1,2-DISUBSTITUTED HYDRAZINES

Elimination of nitrogen by oxidation of the 1,2-disubstituted hydrazines (IIIa) involves two steps, and the azo intermediate is often easily isolable, particularly when either R and R' (or both) is an aromatic group.

$$R\text{—}NH\text{—}NH\text{—}R' \xrightarrow{[O]} R\text{—}N{=}N\text{—}R' \rightarrow R\text{—}R' + RH + N_2 \quad (2\text{–}4)$$

IIIa

A variety of oxidizing agents have been employed in this reaction, including mercuric oxide, ferric chloride, and potassium permanganate. Some 1,2-hydrazines, especially those for which the hydrazine function is incorporated in a cyclic structure, are oxidized to the corresponding azo compound on exposure to air. Many of the intermediate azo compounds have been isolated, and then decomposed by heat or light to yield nitrogen and hydrocarbon products. The nature of the substituents (R and R') in these azo compounds determines their stability. Where R and R' are simple alkyl groups, elevated temperatures are required to evolve nitrogen; certain cyclic and benzyl substituted azo compounds decompose at room temperature; on the other hand, aromatic azo compounds are quite stable. Further discussion of azo compounds will be deferred until Chapter 4.

Dialkylhydrazines react with aliphatic aldehydes to give 1,3,4-oxadiazolidines which can be converted to 1,3,4-triazolidines by reaction with a primary amine.[6]

Two nitrogen atoms joined through a methylene group may be considered a 1,2-disubstituted hydrazine. Recent literature reports[7a] indicate remarkable progress in this area of three-membered ring hydrazines (diaziridines). It has been reported that three-membered ring hydrazines can be readily prepared by a general method employing chloramine and azomethines:

$$R\text{—}CH{=}N\text{—}R' + NH_2Cl \rightarrow R\overset{\displaystyle NH}{\underset{\displaystyle N\text{—}R'}{\diagup}}CH\Big| \qquad (2\text{–}5)$$

The diaziridines dissolve in organic solvents, react slowly with acid, and are stable to alkali and to heat (up to 100°C). As an alternative synthetic method, diazirines (three-membered ring azo compounds) can add Grignard compounds to yield N-alkyl diaziridines; these can then be further hydrolyzed to alkyl hydrazines.[7b]   An analogous reaction of 2-methyldiazirine with ethylmagnesium bromide yields 1-ethyl-2-methyldiaziridine, which can also be prepared from chloramine and ethylidene ethylamine:

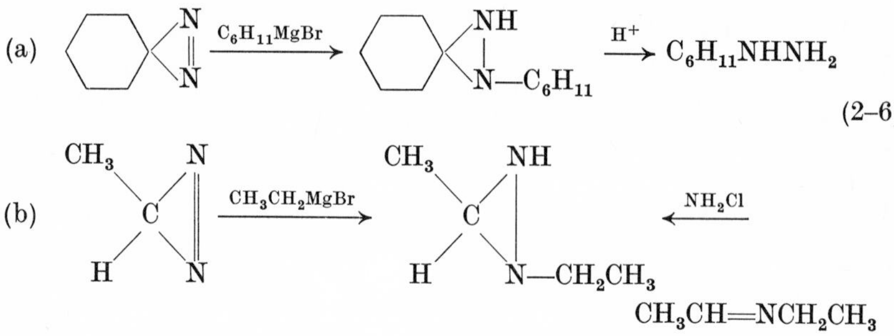

(a) $\underset{N}{\overset{N}{\bigm|\bigm|}}$ ⬡ $\xrightarrow{C_6H_{11}MgBr}$ ⬡ $\overset{NH}{\underset{N-C_6H_{11}}{\bigm|}}$ $\xrightarrow{H^+}$ $C_6H_{11}NHNH_2$

$$(2\text{--}6)$$

(b) $\underset{H \quad N}{\overset{CH_3 \quad N}{\diagdown C \diagup}}\bigm|\bigm|$ $\xrightarrow{CH_3CH_2MgBr}$ $\underset{H \quad N-CH_2CH_3}{\overset{CH_3 \quad NH}{\diagdown C \diagup}}$ $\xleftarrow{NH_2Cl}$

$$CH_3CH{=}NCH_2CH_3$$

Many other examples of cyclic hydrazines, in which both nitrogen atoms are contained in a ring, are known. Discussion of six-membered cyclic hydrazines (e.g. piperidazines) are beyond the scope of this book. A few examples of four-membered ring hydrazines have been reported in the literature, e.g. the reaction of activated olefins with diethyl azodicarboxylate (see also p. 77):

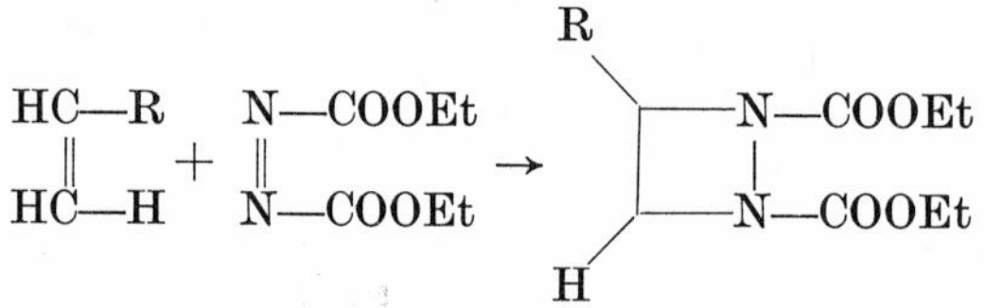

$$\underset{HC-H}{\overset{HC-R}{\bigm|\bigm|}} + \underset{N-COOEt}{\overset{N-COOEt}{\bigm|\bigm|}} \rightarrow \underset{H}{\overset{R}{\bigg\diagup}}\underset{}{\overset{N-COOEt}{\underset{N-COOEt}{\bigm|}}}$$

$$(2\text{--}7)$$

Under the influence of acids, aromatic hydrazines undergo the benzidine-type rearrangements (2–7a). The mechanism of these reactions[8a] has been the subject of intense investigtions and a "proton sandwich" is believed to be involved:[8b]

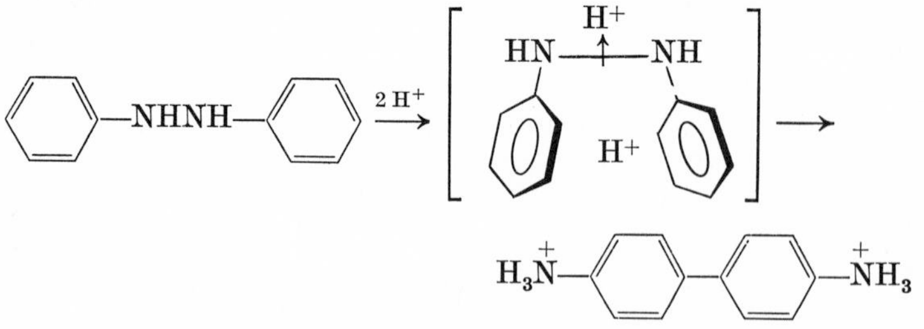

$$(2\text{--}7a)$$

2–3. 1,1-DISUBSTITUTED HYDRAZINES

A primary amine function in 1,1-disubstituted hydrazines (IIIb) permits several reactions which are not possible in the isomeric 1,2-disubstituted hydrazines. Oxidations of 1,1-disubstituted hydrazines can yield two possible products, probably proceeding through an N-nitrene intermediate (see Chapter 7):

$$\underset{\underset{R'}{\overset{R}{\diagdown}}}{N}-NH_2 \overset{[O]}{\longrightarrow} \left[\underset{\underset{R'}{\overset{R}{\diagdown}}}{N}-\overset{..}{\underset{..}{N}}\right] \overset{(a)}{\underset{(b)}{\longrightarrow}} \quad \underset{\underset{R'}{\overset{R}{\diagdown}}}{N}-N=N-\underset{\overset{R}{\diagup}}{\underset{R'}{}}N \qquad (2\text{-}8)$$

IIIb   VI   VII

$$R-R' + N_2$$

Combination of two nitrene moieties or, more likely, reaction of the nitrene with unreacted hydrazine (path a) gives rise to tetrazenes (VII). Decomposition of the nitrene to give nitrogen and a hydrocarbon has been observed also (path b). Products of oxidations are determined by the nature of the substituents (R and R') in IIIb; however, the majority of such oxidations yield the tetrazene VII (2–8a). In some cases, oxidations of 1,1-disubstituted hydrazines proceed directly to give evolution of nitrogen and formation of hydrocarbon products (2–5b). This latter path, termed the "abnormal oxidation,"[9] requires that substituent groups be capable of stabilizing the intermediate fragments as a new carbon-carbon bond is formed. Such groups as benzyl (Equation 2–9) and cyanomethylene exhibit these properties:

$$\phi-CH_2-\underset{\underset{NH_2}{|}}{N}-CH_2\phi + HgO \rightarrow \phi-CH_2CH_2-\phi + N_2 \qquad (2\text{-}9)$$

These abnormal oxidations proceed readily in heterogeneous oxidizing systems (e.g., ethanol-mercuric oxide), with a larger surface area of the oxidizing agent increasing the rate of nitrogen evolution. Similar results with heterogeneous systems have been obtained in other reactions evolving nitrogen.[10] In more homogeneous media, the tetrazene formation is often favored; for example, a method for preparing tetrabenzyltetrazene from dibenzylhydrazine uses mercuric acetate in ethanol solution. A solid surface, then, appears to aid in lowering the energy of activation for nitrogen evolution and probably helps keep the N-nitrene intermediates apart, preventing tetrazene formation. When such groups as methyl, ethyl, cyclohexyl, and similar alkyl groups are present on the 1,1-disubstituted hydrazine, the inability of these alkyl groups to stabilize the intermediate carbon fragments (whether they are ionic or free radical has not been determined) discourages cleavage of the carbon-nitrogen bonds. In these cases, even in homogeneous media, nitrogen formation is not energetically favorable, so tetrazene is formed instead. Compounds such as 1-benzyl-1-butylhydrazine have been oxidized in low yield to n-amylbenzene by mercuric oxide in methylene chloride; however, in ethanol solution this same reaction yields the corresponding tetrazene. Other related variations of the abnormal oxidation include the following: (1) oxidation of N-amino-isoindoline to benzocyclobutene and 1,2-dimethylene-3,5-cyclohadiene,

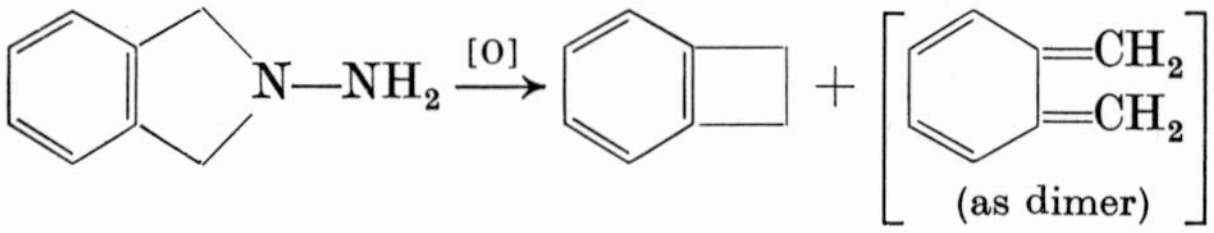

$$(2\text{-}10)$$

(2) oxidation of N-amino-1,3-diphenylisoindoline to 1,2-diphenylbenzo-cyclobutene,[11]

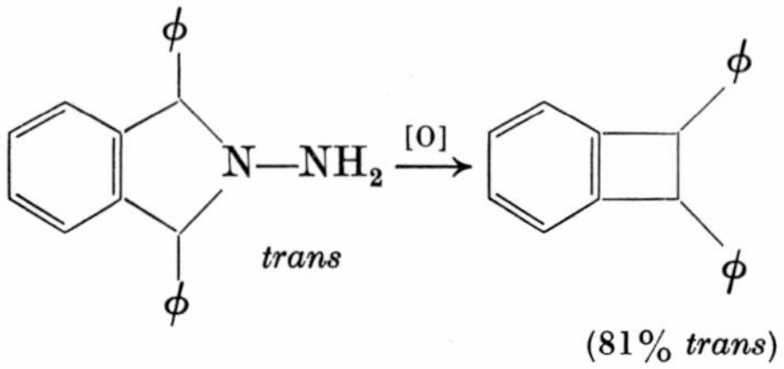

$$(2\text{-}11)$$

(81% *trans*)

(3) oxidation of *cis*- and *trans*-N-amino-2,6-diphenylpiperidines to *cis*- and *trans*-1,2-diphenylcyclopentanes[9] respectively, and the corresponding olefin,

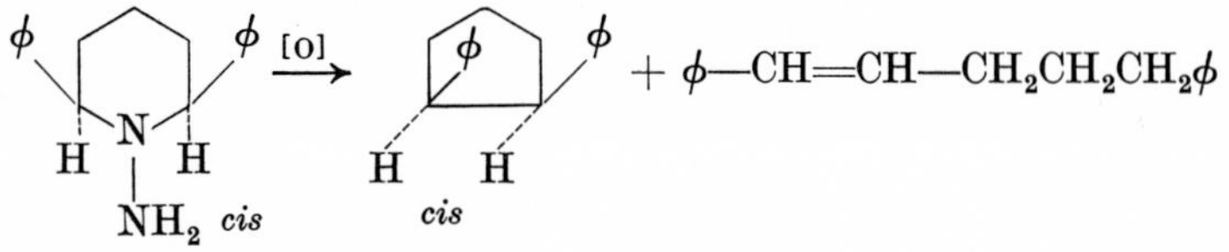

$$(2\text{-}12)$$

A recent preliminary report[12] on oxidations of 1,1-dialkylhydrazines supports and expands the theory that these reactions proceed via a dialkyl-nitrene (dialkyldiazene) which can (1) dimerize to tetrazene, (2) undergo a base catalyzed shift to give alkylhydrazones, (3) alkylate other bases present in the mixture (2–13):

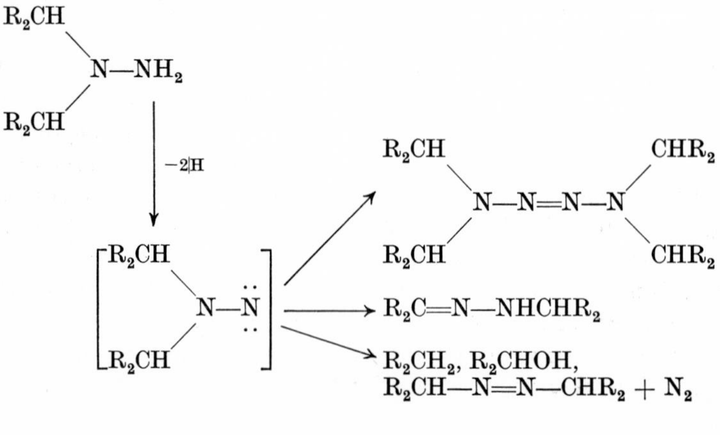

$$(2\text{-}13)$$

When 1,1-dipropylhydrazine is oxidized, major products include the propylhydrazone of propionaldehyde, the dipropylhydrazone of propionaldehyde, and tetrapropyltetrazene. Minor products of this reaction are propanol, azopropane, propane, and nitrogen. It might be noted here that tetrazenes, if heated to a sufficiently high temperature, will lose nitrogen. Other products of this latter decomposition are varied, probably consisting of tetrasubstituted hydrazine and azomethines.

A reaction analogous to the abnormal oxidation of IIIb hydrazines is the basic decomposition of sulfonylhydrazides.[13a,b] These reactions appear to proceed through an N-nitrene identical with that discussed above (2–13), and products are often identical with those obtained by oxidation of the corresponding hydrazines (2–14):

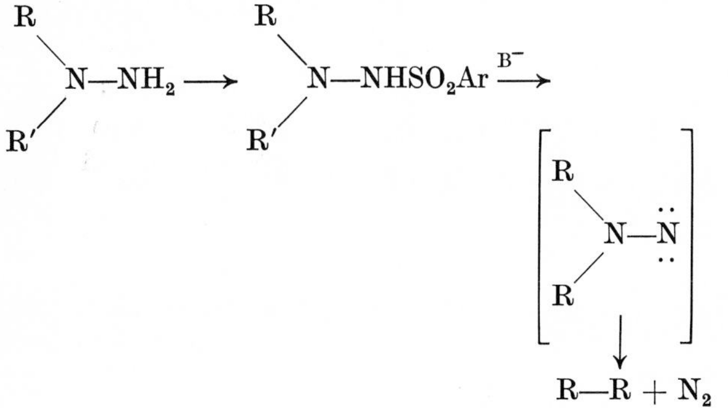

$$\text{VIII}$$

Here, as in the abnormal oxidations, stabilizing R groups (e.g. benzyl) are desirable to obtain nitrogen and a hydrocarbon product. Similarly, treatment of certain nitrosamines with sodium hydrosulfite in basic media yields nitrogen and a hydrocarbon product. An N-nitrene intermediate has been proposed[9] for this reaction, since products are identical with those obtained by mercuric oxide oxidation of the corresponding hydrazine:

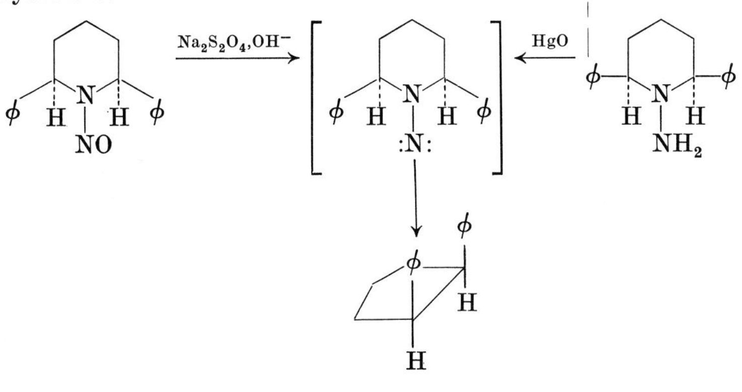

$$(2-15)$$

The primary amine function in 1,1-disubstituted hydrazines allows certain other reactions that are not possible with the 1,2-disubstituted hydrazines. For example, the 1,1-hydrazines react with carbonyl derivatives to form hydrazones, and nitrous acid deaminates a 1,1-hydrazine to give nitrogen and a secondary amine.

A convenient method for aminating secondary and tertiary amines to produce hydrazines or hydrazinium salts has been described[14] utilizing hydroxylamine-O-sulfonic acid:

$$NH_2OSO_3H + R_2NH \rightarrow R_2N{-}NH_2 + H_2SO_4 \qquad (2\text{--}16)$$

This reagent is a convenient source of the NH_2^+ moiety and may find wider use in the future.

Tetrasubstituted hydrazines (V) have received less attention than other classes of hydrazines. Tetraphenylhydrazine is interesting, however, since it exhibits peculiar properties due to the crowding of the bulky phenyl groups around the small nitrogen atoms. Even at the temperature of liquid air, tetraphenylhydrazine decomposes in the presence of acid to form ions and possibly some radicals:

$$2 \; {}^{\phi}_{\phi}\!\!>\!\!N{-}N\!\!<^{\phi}_{\phi} + H^+ \rightarrow \; {}^{\phi}_{\phi}\!\!>\!\!\overset{+}{N} + \; {}^{\phi}_{\phi}\!\!>\!\!N{-}H + 2 \; {}^{\phi}_{\phi}\!\!>\!\!N\cdot \qquad (2\text{--}17)$$

Evidently, this nitrogen-nitrogen bond is weakened by the steric crowding in this compound, since other tetrasubstituted hydrazines are quite stable to acid. The cyclic chloramine from ethyleneimine has been used to couple two nitrogen atoms in forming 1,1-biaziridine (IX), illustrating a useful path to other tetrasubstituted hydrazines:

$$\triangleright\!\!NH \xrightarrow{\text{NaOCl}} \triangleright\!\!N{-}Cl \xrightarrow{\triangleright N^-Li^+} \triangleright\!\!N{-}N\!\!\triangleleft \qquad (2\text{--}18)$$

IX

The hydrazine IX is only feebly basic and decomposes explosively in the presence of heat and oxygen.

2–4. HYDRAZINIUM SALTS[15]

Monosubstituted alkyl hydrazines are alkylated by simple alkyl halides at the substituted nitrogen atom, provided steric effects do not interfere. A 1,1,1-trisubstituted hydrazine (hydrazinium salt) results when hydrazine is reacted with an excess of a simple alkyl halide such as methyl iodide. Larger alkyl groups such as isopropyl prevent the grouping of three alkyl groups around a single nitrogen atom, often yielding mixtures of mono-, di- and 1,2-substituted hydrazines. A superior preparation of hydrazinium salts, one which allows greater variation in the R groups, involves the treatment of a tertiary amine with chloramine:[16]

$$R_3N + NH_2Cl \rightarrow R_3\overset{+}{N}\!-\!NH_2Cl^- \tag{2-19}$$

The usual electron-donating properties of alkyl groups has led some workers to predict a higher basicity (and consequent lower acidity for the protonated form) for the substituted hydrazines than that of hydrazine itself. However, contrary to expected behavior, methylation of hydrazine does not increase basicity; hydrazine hydrochloride is a weaker acid (stronger base) (pK$_a$ 7.95, 8.1) than methylhydrazine hydrochloride (pK$_a$ 7.87), which in turn is a weaker acid than dimethylhydrazine hydrochloride (pK$_a$ 7.21).[17] These apparently anomalous acidity values for hydrazine hydrochlorides may possibly be explained as follows: the protonated form of 1,1-dimethylhydrazine places the 1-nitrogen atom into the tetrahedral configuration, which forces a steric interaction between the methyl groups and the 2-amino nitrogen. Loss of a proton and consequent loss of the tetrahedral configuration helps to relieve the strain in the molecule. Since the strain of tetrahedral configuration is greater in dimethylhydrazine than it is in methylhydrazine, and greater still than in hydrazine itself, the loss of a proton will be more energetically favored in the case of dimethylhydrazine hydrochloride than in either methylhydrazine or hydrazine hydrochlorides. The equilibrium in Equation 2–20 is thereby displaced to the right, and this increases the acidity of dimethylhydrazine hydrochloride:

$$\overset{\displaystyle H}{\underset{\displaystyle +}{(CH_3)_2\overset{|}{N}\!-\!NH_2}} \rightleftharpoons (CH_3)_2N\!-\!NH_2 + H^+ \tag{2-20}$$

Since the experimental facts show that further alkylation of alkyl hydrazines takes place on the substituted nitrogen atom, the conclusion must be drawn that the substituted nitrogen is *less* basic but *more* nucleophilic than an unsubstituted hydrazine nitrogen atom.

Alkyl hydrazines have been studied[18] under conditions of the Mannich reaction. The reaction of the hydrochloride of 1,2-dialkylhydrazines with formaldehyde and acetophenone yields 3-phenyl-1,2-dialkyl-Δ^3-pyrazolines:

$$\phi COCH_3 + (CH_2O)_x + R\!-\!NH\!-\!NH\!-\!R \rightarrow \left[\phi\!-\!\underset{\displaystyle O}{\overset{\displaystyle R}{\underset{\displaystyle \|}{\overset{\displaystyle |}{C}}}}\!-\!CH_2CH_2\overset{|}{N}\!-\!NH\!-\!R \right]$$

$$HCl$$

$$\tag{2-21}$$

2–5. REDUCTION WITH HYDRAZINE

The reducing power of hydrazine has been put to use in a variety of systems. A thorough review of the hydrazine-oxygen reduction of olefinic compounds is available.[16,19,26] In this system, which is especially useful for reducing the unsaturated portion of olefinic acids, oxygen, introduced by vigorous stirring in air, is a necessary component. Under a pure nitrogen atmosphere no reduction was observed, while a temperature of approximately 50° C and a narrow range of alkalinity produced optimum yields. A proposed intermediate diimide in the hydrazine-oxygen system has received strong support from the work of others in related systems.[20,21] By using systems of hydrazine plus an oxidant, it has been shown that olefinic compounds can be reduced with *cis* addition of hydrogen atoms, probably via a cyclic intermediate (2–22a); Equation (2–22b) illustrates the stereospecificity of the method:

$$\text{(b)} \quad \phi\text{—C}\equiv\text{C—COOH} \rightarrow \phi\text{—CH}=\text{CH—COOH} \text{ (mostly } cis\text{)}$$

Traces of cupric ion have been shown to be effective in promoting these reductions. The selectivity of diimide, produced by various techniques, for unsaturated bonds is illustrated by its ability to reduce allyl disulfide to propyl disulfide.

Evidence for the production of diimide from hydrazine was obtained by mass spectrographic studies of an electrical discharge through hydrazine.[22] The ability to reduce olefinic bonds under mild conditions in an alkaline solution suggests that any reaction involving hydrazine and an olefinic compound in the presence of oxygen must take into account the possibility of reduction of the olefinic material by the transient production of diimide. This problem can, of course, be avoided by carrying out such a reaction under an atmosphere of nitrogen.

Reductive cleavage of the nitrogen-nitrogen bond by strong reducing agents has been observed in several 1,2-disubstituted hydrazines (e.g., hydrazobenzene is cleaved to aniline). Raney nickel and hydrazine has been studied[23a] thoroughly. Conditions as mild as refluxing methanol serve to cleave the N—N bond in a variety of hydrazines as well as cleaving N,N'-diacylhydrazines to amides. This same reducing system has been used to convert nitro compounds to amines.[23b,c] Similarly, a convenient preparation of primary amines from nitriles using hydrazine hydrate–Raney nickel in alcohol has been reported:[23d]

$$R—C{\equiv}N + NH_2NH_2 \xrightarrow{\text{Raney Ni}} RCH_2NH_2 \qquad (2\text{-}23)$$

The strong nucleophilic nature of hydrazine and alkyl hydrazines manifests itself in a variety of reactions. Thus, a number of activated aromatic halides can be made to react with hydrazine to form arylhydrazines:

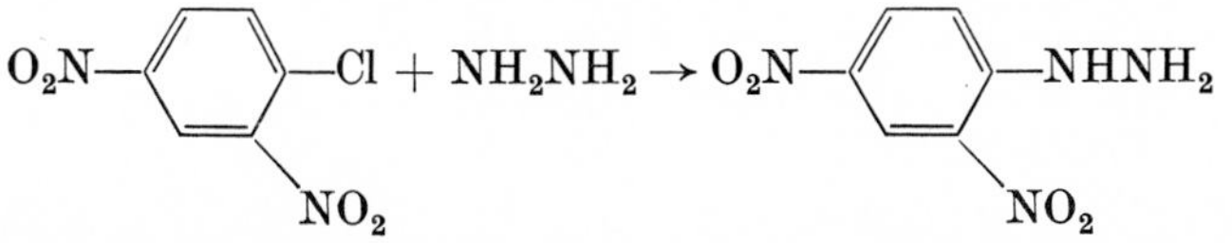

$$O_2N—\langle\ \rangle—Cl + NH_2NH_2 \rightarrow O_2N—\langle\ \rangle—NHNH_2 \quad (2\text{-}24)$$

Similarly, hydrazine attacks electron deficient olefins such as α,β-unsaturated esters and proceeds further to cyclize to pyrazolidinones:

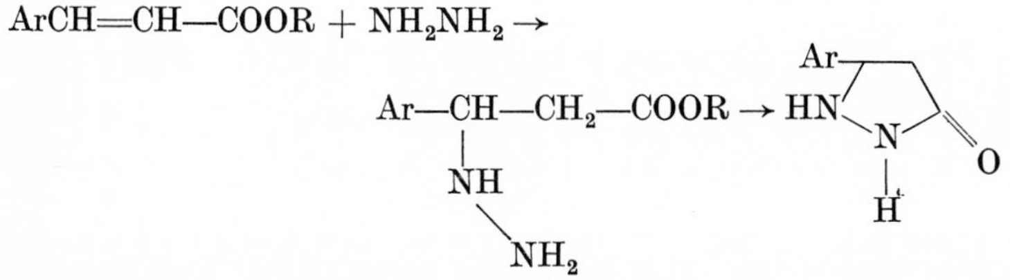

$$ArCH{=}CH—COOR + NH_2NH_2 \rightarrow$$

$$Ar—CH—CH_2—COOR \rightarrow HN \qquad (2\text{-}25)$$
$$\underset{\underset{NH_2}{|}}{NH}$$

An interesting variation on the above reaction has been reported for the reaction between 1,1-dialkylhydrazines and acrolein. Here, initial attack by the more nucleophilic trisubstituted nitrogen atom followed by cyclization leads to a quaternary pyrazolinium salt. Mild decomposition of the intermediate salt by base cleaves the N—N bond, yielding a β-aminonitrile:[24]

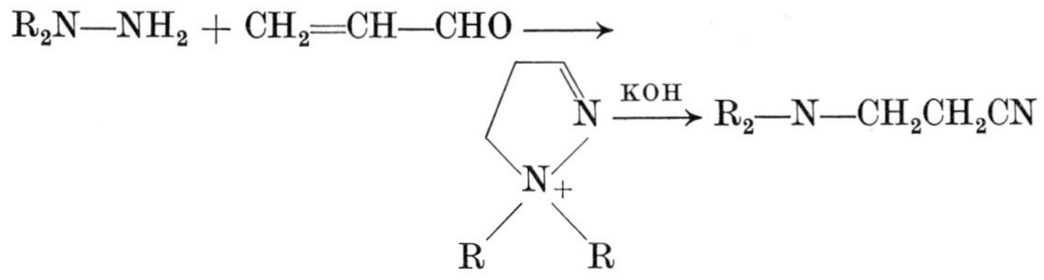

$$R_2N—NH_2 + CH_2{=}CH—CHO \longrightarrow$$

$$\xrightarrow{\text{KOH}} R_2—N—CH_2CH_2CN \qquad (2\text{-}26)$$

The reactions of sodium hydrazine ($NaNHNH_2$) with various compounds have been investigated by Kauffmann and co-workers.[25] The versatility of this reagent promises its wider use in the future.

REFERENCES

General

L. F. AUDRIETH and B. A. OGG, *The Chemistry of Hydrazine*, John Wiley and Sons, Inc., New York, 1951.

H. WIELAND, *Die Hydrazine*, Verlag F. Enke, Stuttgart, 1913.

A. N. KOST and R. N. SAGITULLIN, Monoalkylhydrazines, *Russ. Chem. Rev.*, **1964,** 159.

H. H. Sisler, G. M. Omietanski, and B. Rudner, The chemistry of quaternized hydrazine compounds, *Chem. Rev.*, **57,** 1021 (1957).

Text

1. (a) A. N. Kost and R. S. Sagitullin, *Russ. Chem. Rev.*, **1964,** 159.
    (b) A. Furst, R. C. Berlo, and S. Hooton, *Chem. Rev.*, **65,** 51 (1965).
    (c) E. Jucker, *Angew. Chem.*, **71,** 321 (1959).
2. L. F. Audrieth and B. A. Ogg, *The Chemistry of Hydrazine*, John Wiley and Sons, Inc., New York, 1951.
3. F. Degering (ed.), *An Outline of Organic Nitrogen Compounds*, University Litho-printers, Ypsilanti, Michigan, 1950, pp. 376ff.
4. R. Wagner and H. Zook, *Synthetic Organic Chemistry*, John Wiley and Sons, Inc., New York, 1956.
5. (a) R. F. Evans, *Rev. Pure Appl. Chem.*, **12,** 146 (1962).
    (b) A. Ebnother, E. Jücker, A. Lindenmann, E. Rissi, R. Steiner, R. Suess, and A. Vogel, *Helv. Chim. Acta*, **42,** 533 (1959).
6. J. Strating *et al.*, *Rec. Trav. Chim.*, **84,** 408 (1965) and previous papers.
7. (a) E. Schmitz and R. Ohme, *Chem. Ber.*, **94,** 2166 (1961); E. Schmitz, *ibid.*, **95,** 676 (1962).
    (b) E. Schmitz and R. Ohme, *Angew. Chem.*, **73,** 220 (1961); E. Schmitz, *ibid.*, **76,** 197 (1964).
8. (a) M. Vecera, *Chem. Listy* **52,** 1373 (1958); M. J. S. Dewar, in P. de Mayo, *Molecular Rearrangements*, John Wiley and Sons, Inc., New York, 1963, p. 323.
    (b) L. L. Ferstandig, *Tetrahedron Letters*, 1235 (1963).
9. C. G. Overberger, J. G. Lombardino, and R. G. Hiskey, *J. Am. Chem. Soc.*, **79,** 1510, 6430 (1957); *ibid.*, **80,** 3009 (1958); see also D. M. King and A. J. Bard, *ibid.*, **87,** 419 (1965) and C. D. Campbell and C. W. Rees, *Proc. Chem. Soc.*, 296 (1964).
10. M. S. Newman and E. Caflish, *J. Am. Chem. Soc.*, **80,** 862 (1958).
11. L. H. Carpino, *ibid.*, **82,** 2728 (1960); *J. Am. Chem. Soc.*, **84,** 2196 (1962).
12. W. Urry and C. Ikoku, American Chemical Society Abstracts, January 1964 Meeting, p. 25c.
13. (a) L. Carpino, *J. Am. Chem. Soc.*, **79,** 98, 4427 (1957).
    (b) R. L. Hinman and K. Hamm, *ibid.*, **81,** 3294 (1959).
14. R. Gosl and A. Mewsen, *Chem. Ber.*, **92,** 2521 (1959).
15. H. H. Sisler, G. M. Omietanski and B. Rudner, *Chem. Rev.*, **57,** 1021 (1957).
16. G. M. Omietanski and H. H. Sisler, *J. Am. Chem. Soc.*, **78,** 1211 (1956).
17. R. L. Hinman, *J. Org. Chem.*, **23,** 1587 (1958).
18. R. L. Hinman, R. D. Ellefson, and R. D. Campbell, *J. Am. Chem. Soc.*, **82,** 3988 (1960).
19. S. Aylward and N. Sawistowska, *Chem. Ind. (London)*, 484 (1962).
20. E. J. Corey, W. L. Mock, and D. J. Pasto, *J. Am. Chem. Soc.*, **83,** 2957 (1961).
21. S. Hünig, H. R. Müller, and W. Thier, *Tetrahedron Letters*, No. 11, 353 (1961).
22. S. N. Foner and R. L. Hudson, *J. Chem. Phys.*, **28,** 719 (1958).
23. (a) D. Robinson and R. K. Brown, *Can. J. Chem.*, **39,** 1171 (1961).
    (b) L. P. Kuhn, *J. Am. Chem. Soc.*, **73,** 1510 (1951).
    (c) B. Balcom and A. Furst, *J. Am. Chem. Soc.*, **75,** 4334 (1953).
    (d) A. P. Terent'ev *et al.*, *Khim. Nauka i Promy.*, **4,** 281 (1959); *C.A.*, **53,** 21879 (1959).
24. B. V. Ioffe and K. N. Zelenin, *Proc. Acad. Sci. USSR*, **134,** 1094 (1960); *C.A.*, **55,** 8284i (1961); *Tetrahedron Letters*, 481 (1962).
25. T. Kauffmann, *Angew. Chem.*, **76,** 206 (1964).
26. S. Hünig, H. R. Müller, and W. Thier, *Angew. Chem.*, **77,** 368 (1965).

3
Azomethines with Nitrogen-Nitrogen Bonds

3–1. HYDRAZONES AND AZINES; FORMATION AND REACTIONS

Derivatives of hydrazine containing at least one primary amine function add to the carbonyl groups of aldehydes and ketones. A free electron pair on the terminal nitrogen atom initiates attack on the polarized carbonyl function, followed by elimination of water:

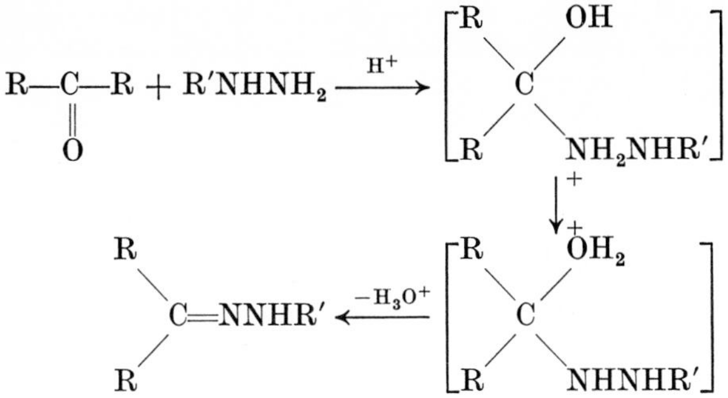

$$R—\overset{\underset{\displaystyle \parallel}{}}{\underset{O}{C}}—R + R'NHNH_2 \xrightarrow{H^+} \left[\begin{array}{c} R \\ \diagdown \\ C \\ \diagup \\ R \end{array} \begin{array}{c} OH \\ \\ \\ \\ NH_2NHR' \end{array} \right] \tag{3-1}$$

$$\begin{array}{c} R \\ \diagdown \\ C=NNHR' \\ \diagup \\ R \end{array} \xleftarrow{-H_3O^+} \left[\begin{array}{c} R \\ \diagdown \\ C \\ \diagup \\ R \end{array} \begin{array}{c} \overset{+}{O}H_2 \\ \\ \\ NHNHR' \end{array} \right]$$

Acid catalysts promote the first step in 3–1 by forming the conjugate acid of the ketone, further polarizing the carbonyl group. This reaction has been found very useful for converting many liquid aldehydes and ketones to solid hydrazones;[1] melting points for solid 2,4-dinitrophenylhydrazones have been tabulated. A fixed geometry about the carbon-nitrogen double bond allows geometric (*syn-anti*) isomerism in these compounds:

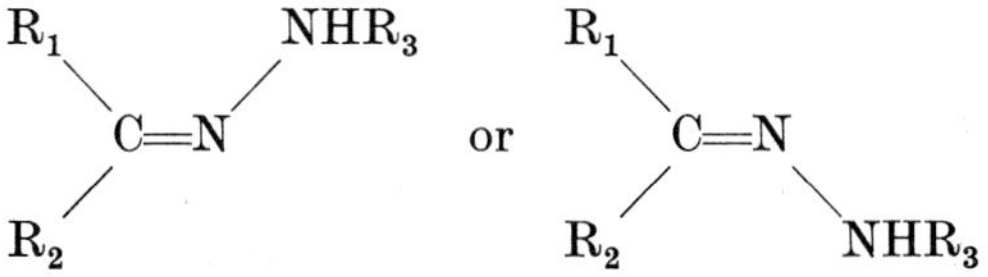

$$\begin{array}{c} R_1 \\ \diagdown \\ C=N \\ \diagup \\ R_2 \end{array} \begin{array}{c} NHR_3 \\ \diagup \\ \\ \end{array} \quad \text{or} \quad \begin{array}{c} R_1 \\ \diagdown \\ C=N \\ \diagup \\ R_2 \end{array} \begin{array}{c} \\ \\ \diagdown \\ NHR_3 \end{array}$$

Examples of successful separation of the two possible diastereomeric compounds have been recorded; for example, reaction of p-butylphenyl-glyoxylic acid with p-tolylhydrazine yields two products[2] having different melting points, ultraviolet spectra, and acidity constants:

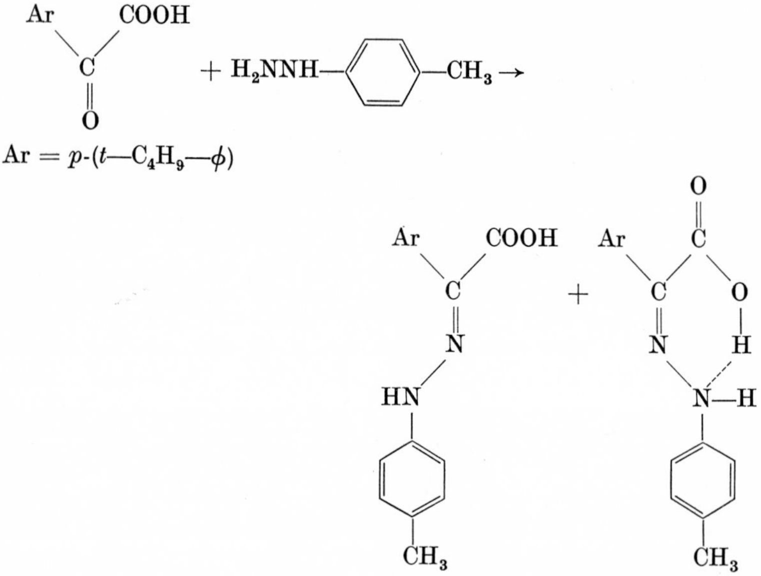

$$Ar{\diagdown}C{\diagup}COOH \quad + \; H_2NNH-\!\!\langle\!\!\bigcirc\!\!\rangle\!\!-CH_3 \rightarrow$$

with $C=O$ below the central carbon.

$Ar = p\text{-}(t\text{---}C_4H_9\text{---}\phi)$

$$
\begin{array}{cc}
\text{anti (A)} & \text{syn (B)} \\
\text{m.p. } 135°\text{--}137°C & \text{m.p. } 118°\text{--}120°C \\
pK_a = 6.6 & pK_a = 5.1
\end{array}
$$

(3–2)

In this case, spatial arrangement of neighboring groups affects the acidity of the carboxyl group, probably through hydrogen bonding in the *syn* form, which facilitates ionization of the carboxyl function.

Hydrazones derived from ketones or aldehydes by reaction of one mole of hydrazine with one mole of carbonyl compound may be converted to hydro-carbons by the Wolff-Kishner reduction. In this reaction, a hydrazone is treated in ethylene glycol solution with potassium hydroxide to yield nitrogen and a hydrocarbon:

$$\underset{\underset{NH_2}{\overset{|}{N}}}{\overset{\displaystyle R{-}\underset{\|}{C}{-}R'}{}} \quad + \; KOH \rightarrow RCH_2R' + N_2 \tag{3–3}$$

Kinetic studies[3] of the Wolff-Kishner reaction on the hydrazones of diaryl ketones revealed a first-order dependence on base *and* a first-order dependence on hydrazone; the following mechanism for the over-all reaction has been proposed:

$$R_2C{=}N{-}NH_2 + B^- \rightleftharpoons R_2C{=}N{-}NH^- + BH \text{ (fast)}$$

$$R_2C{=}NNH^- \qquad\quad \rightleftharpoons R_2CH{-}N{=}N^- \text{ (slow)}$$

$$R_2CH{-}N{=}N^- \qquad \rightleftharpoons R_2CH^- + N_2 \text{ (fast)} \qquad\qquad (3\text{-}4)$$

$$R_2CH^- + BH \qquad\quad \rightleftharpoons R_2CH_2 + B^- \text{ (fast)}$$

In this sequence the second, *rate-determining* step is a tautomeric shift to give the unstable anion of a substituted diimide. An interesting reduction of this type under very mild conditions[4a] occurs when ethyl 3-indolyloxalate is treated with hydrazine hydrate in the absence of potassium hydroxide. Isolation of indole-3-acethydrazide from this reaction indicates an unexpected reduction of the α-carbonyl, possibly through a Wolff-Kishner-type intermediate; α-halo ketones give the corresponding olefins upon treatment with hydrazine.[4b]

A number of ketohydrazones have been converted to azoacetates by the action of lead tetraacetate[5] under very mild conditions:

$$R_1R_2C{=}N{-}NH{-}R_3 + Pb(OAc)_4 \rightarrow R_1R_2C \begin{smallmatrix} \nearrow N{=}N{-}R_3 \\ \\ \searrow O{-}\underset{\underset{O}{\|}}{C}{-}CH_3 \end{smallmatrix} \qquad (3\text{-}5)$$

A mechanism involving abstraction of the relatively reactive hydrogen atom on nitrogen in a slow, rate-determining step has been postulated. Rearrangement to an azo compound, followed by acetoxy abstraction by a carbon radical, gives the azoacetates.[5]

The class of dihydrazones known as azines are readily prepared from reaction of hydrazine with *two* moles of an aldehyde or ketone:

$$2 R{-}\underset{\underset{O}{\|}}{C}{-}R + NH_2NH_2 \rightarrow \underset{R}{\overset{R}{\diagdown}}C{=}N{-}N{=}C\underset{R}{\overset{R}{\diagup}} \qquad (3\text{-}6)$$

Aldehydes react very rapidly with hydrazine under ordinary conditions, forming first an aldehyde hydrazone, followed by a faster condensation with a second mole of aldehyde to yield an azine. Aldehyde hydrazones can be isolated only if careful, mild conditions and an excess of hydrazine are employed.

By employing a 1,4-addition of halogen (e.g. chlorine) to appropriate azines, an intermediate azo compound can be prepared:[6]

$$
\begin{array}{c}
\text{Ar} \\
\diagdown \\
\quad\text{C}\!=\!\text{N}\!-\!\text{N}\!=\!\text{C} \\
\diagup \\
\text{R}
\end{array}
\begin{array}{c}
\text{Ar} \\
\diagup \\
\\
\diagdown \\
\text{R}
\end{array}
+ \text{Cl}_2 \longrightarrow
\begin{array}{c}
\text{Ar} \\
\diagdown \\
\quad\text{C}\!-\!\text{N}\!=\!\text{N}\!-\!\text{C} \\
\diagup \quad | \\
\text{R} \quad \text{Cl}
\end{array}
\begin{array}{c}
\text{Ar} \\
\diagup \\
\\
| \quad \diagdown \\
\text{Cl} \quad \text{R}
\end{array}
$$

$$
\xrightarrow{\ \Delta\ }
\begin{array}{c}
\text{Ar} \quad\quad \text{Ar} \\
\diagdown \quad\quad \diagup \\
\text{C}\!-\!\text{C} \\
\diagup \; | \quad | \; \diagdown \\
\text{R} \;\; \text{Cl} \;\; \text{Cl} \;\; \text{R}
\end{array}
+ \text{N}_2 \qquad (3\text{--}7)
$$

Thermal decomposition of the azo compound yields the expected coupled dihalide, while in the presence of zinc chloride the azo compound yields an indene. Reaction (3–6) serves as a source of symmetrically substituted hydrazines since reduction of the azines affords the corresponding 1,2-disubstituted hydrazines.

Condensation of formaldehyde with hydrazine gives rise to a polymeric material. However, heating of the polymer under an inert atmosphere gives the monomeric formaldehyde azine, a very reactive material stable only at low temperature.[7]

Diketones have been reacted with hydrazine to afford cyclic azines or their isomeric equivalents; 1,3- and 1,4-diketones have been used to prepare pyrazoles, dihydropyridazines and pyrroles (3–8a and b):

(a) $\quad$ $\text{NH}_2\text{NH}_2 + \text{R}\!-\!\underset{\underset{\text{O}}{\|}}{\text{C}}\!-\!\text{CH}_2\!-\!\underset{\underset{\text{O}}{\|}}{\text{C}}\!-\!\text{R} \rightarrow$

$$(3\text{--}8)$$

(b) $\ \text{R}\!-\!\underset{\underset{\text{O}}{\|}}{\text{C}}\!-\!\text{CH}_2\!-\!\text{CH}_2\underset{\underset{\text{O}}{\|}}{\text{C}}\!-\!\text{R} + \text{NH}_2\text{NH}_2 \rightarrow$

Still larger ring systems have been made by condensing α, ω-diaroylalkanes with hydrazine:[8]

$$
\text{Ar}\!-\!\underset{\underset{\text{O}}{\|}}{\text{C}}\!-\!(\text{CH}_2)_n\!-\!\underset{\underset{\text{O}}{\|}}{\text{C}}\!-\!\text{Ar} + \text{NH}_2\text{NH}_2 \rightarrow
\begin{array}{c}
(\text{CH}_2)_n \\
\diagup \quad\quad \diagdown \\
\text{Ar}\!-\!\text{C} \quad\quad \text{C}\!-\!\text{Ar} \\
\diagdown\!\diagdown \quad \diagup\!\diagup \\
\text{N}\!-\!\text{N} \quad n = 3, 4
\end{array}
\qquad (3\text{--}9)
$$

Eighteen, twenty, twenty-four, and twenty-eight-membered cyclic bis-azines have been prepared[8] by using a high-dilution technique.

Oxidations of hydrazones are reported to yield aldehydes and nitrogen gas, although yields are often unsatisfactory:

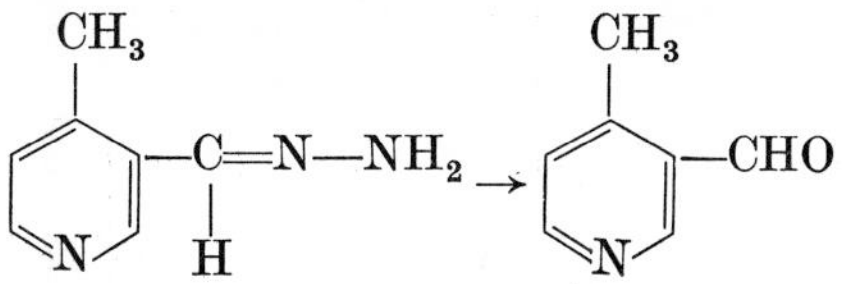

$$(3\text{-}10)$$

Dihydrazones of α-diketones have been oxidized to acetylene compounds, probably proceeding through the bis-diazo compound:

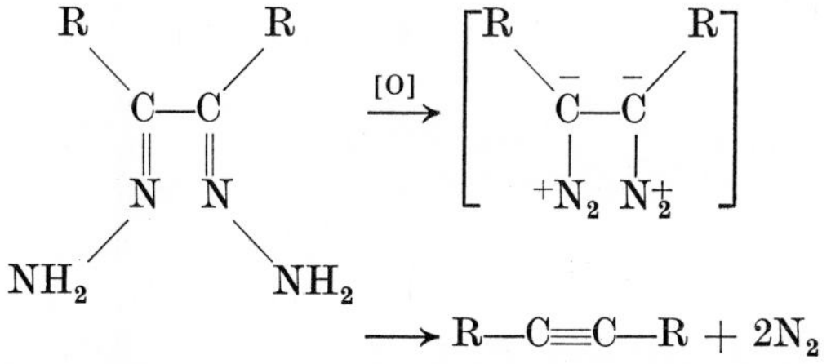

$$\longrightarrow R\text{---}C\equiv C\text{---}R + 2N_2 \qquad (3\text{-}11)$$

Formazans are prepared by reacting a diazonium salt with the azomethine first formed by reacting an aldehyde and a hydrazine:

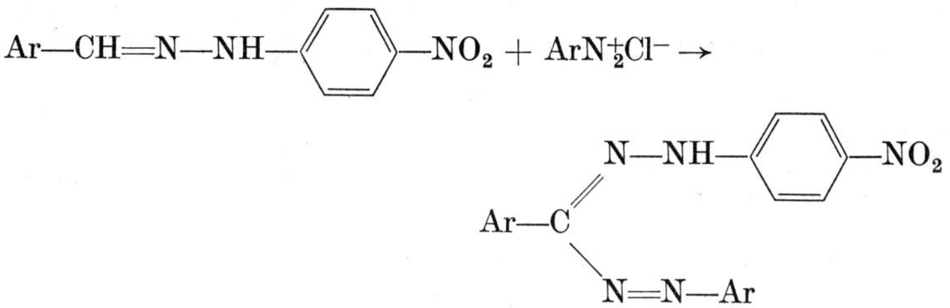

$$Ar\text{---}CH\text{=}N\text{---}NH\text{---}\langle\ \rangle\text{---}NO_2 + ArN_2^+Cl^- \rightarrow$$

$$(3\text{-}12)$$

The products are of particular interest because of their facile conversion (by oxidation) to tetrazolium salts:

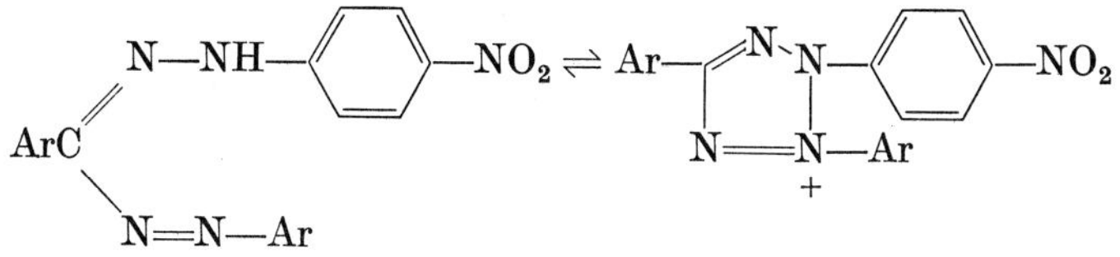

$$(3\text{-}13)$$

These tetrazolium salts are highly colored, and various analytical techniques make use of the equilibrium expressed in Equation (3-13) for rapid colorimetric detection and estimation of either reducible or oxidizable functions.

3-2. OSAZONES

This brief discussion of products resulting from reaction of hydrazine derivatives with carbonyl compounds must include the osazones, compounds derived by reacting a sugar with phenylhydrazine. Isolation and identification of the various sugars were greatly simplified by the discovery of these compounds:

$$
\begin{array}{ccc}
\text{CHO} & \text{NHNH}_2 & \text{CH}=\text{N}-\text{NH}-\bigcirc \\
| & & | \\
\text{CHOH} & & \text{CHOH} \\
| & +\,3\,\bigcirc & \rightarrow \quad | \qquad\qquad \rightarrow \\
(\text{CHOH})_3 & & (\text{CHOH})_3 \\
| & & | \\
\text{CH}_2\text{OH} & & \text{CH}_2\text{OH} \\
\text{Glucose} & &
\end{array}
$$

(3-14)

$$
\begin{array}{c}
\text{CH}=\text{N}-\text{NH}-\bigcirc \qquad \text{NH}_2 + \text{NH}_3 \\
| \\
\text{CH}=\text{N}-\text{NH}-\bigcirc \;+\; \bigcirc \\
| \\
(\text{CHOH})_3 \\
| \\
\text{CH}_2\text{OH} \\
\text{Glucosazone}
\end{array}
$$

In this process, two moles of phenylhydrazine react to form two azomethine links, and a third mole serves to oxidize the hydroxyl group adjacent to the aldehyde function. Rate of formation of the osazone under a given set of conditions varies from one sugar to another, serving as a further means of identifying a particular sugar. Formation of osazones is a general property of α-hydroxy ketones; for example, benzoin and acetoin also undergo the reaction.

An interesting method for converting aldehydes to nitriles via their hydrazonium salts has recently been reported:[9]

$$
\text{RCHO} + (\text{CH}_3)_2\text{N}-\text{NH}_2 \longrightarrow \text{RCH}=\text{N}-\text{N} \underset{\text{CH}_3}{\overset{\text{CH}_3}{\Big\langle}} \xrightarrow{\text{CH}_3\text{I}}
$$

$$
\text{RCH}=\text{N}-\overset{+}{\underset{|}{\text{N}}}-\text{CH}_3 \quad (3\text{-}15)
$$

$$
\overset{\text{CH}_3}{\underset{\text{CH}_3 \;\; \text{I}^-}{}}
$$

$$
\Big\downarrow \text{base}
$$

$$
\text{RC}\equiv\text{N} + (\text{CH}_3)_3\text{N}
$$

The technique takes advantage of the weak N—N bond in the quaternary hydrazone; this bond breaks readily, following proton abstraction (at the carbon atom) by base. Good yields, easy preparation of intermediates, and application to both alkyl or aryl aldehydes make this a convenient method for the preparation of nitriles.

Recent improvements[10] in the Bamford-Stevens technique for preparing aryldiazoalkanes by decomposing p-toluenesulfonylhydrazones with base seem to offer promise of extending the usefulness of this reaction (however, see Chapter 5):

$$\text{ArCH}=\text{N}-\text{NH}-\text{SO}_2-\underset{}{\bigcirc}-\text{CH}_3 \xrightarrow{\text{B}^-}$$

$$\text{ArCHN}_2 + \text{CH}_3-\bigcirc-\text{SO}_2^- + \text{BH}$$

$$(3\text{–}16)$$

Ready availability of the necessary hydrazones and reasonable yields of aryldiazoalkanes may make this a useful method. Discussion of direct oxidation of hydrazones to diazoalkanes is deferred to Chapter 5.

The rapidity and ease with which the hydrazine derivatives react with a variety of carbonyl compounds to form azomethines makes these reactions particularly convenient for derivatizing and characterizing carbonyl compounds. The resulting hydrazones, azines, etc., are themselves of interest for the many unique reactions which they undergo.

REFERENCES

General

N. Nino, Chemistry and analytical behavior of hydrazones, *Formatsiya (Sofia)* **12**, No. 2, 21–26 (1962).

A. N. Kost and I. I. Grandberg, Aldazines and ketazines, *Usp. Khim.*, **28**, 921 (1959).

Text

1. R. Shriner and R. Fuson, *Systematic Identification of Organic Compounds*, 3d ed., John Wiley and Sons, Inc., New York, 1948.
2. C. Vogel and M. Matter, *Helv. Chim. Acta*, **42**, 527 (1959).
3. H. Szmant, H. Harnsberger, T. Butler, and W. Barie, *J. Am. Chem. Soc.*, **74**, 2724 (1952).
4. (a) J. Szmuszkovicz, *J. Med. Pharm. Chem.*, **4**, 274 (1961).
   (b) P. S. Wharton, S. Dunny, and L. S. Krebs, *J. Org. Chem.*, **29**, 958 (1964); see also N. J. Leonard and S. Gelfand, *J. Am. Chem. Soc.*, **77**, 3269 (1955).
5. D. C. Iffland, L. Salisbury, and W. R. Schafer, *J. Am. Chem. Soc.*, **83**, 747 (1961).
6. S. Goldschmidt and B. Acksteiner, *Chem. Ber.*, **91**, 502 (1958).
7. N. P. Neureiter, *J. Am. Chem. Soc.*, **81**, 2910 (1959).
8. C. G. Overberger and I. Tashlick, *J. Am. Chem. Soc.*, **81**, 217 (1959); C. G. Overberger and M. Lapkin, *ibid.*, **77**, 4651 (1955); and others.
9. R. F. Smith and L. E. Walter, *J. Org. Chem.*, **27**, 4372 (1962).
10. D. G. Farnum, *J. Org. Chem.*, **28**, 870 (1963); G. L. Closs and R. A. Moss, *J. Am. Chem. Soc.*, **86**, 4042 (1964); H. Shechter et al., *ibid.*, **87**, 935 (1965).

4

Azo Compounds

4-1. INTRODUCTION

Azo compounds (I) are characterized by the presence of the unsaturated nitrogen-nitrogen group (—N=N—). The aromatic azo compounds, where R and R' are aromatic substituents, are highly colored compounds, thus explaining their widespread utilization in the dye industry:

$$R—N=N—R'$$

I

In contrast, most aliphatic azo compounds in which either R or R' (or both) is an aliphatic group are colorless. Further differences exist in the methods of preparation and in the properties of aliphatic and aromatic azo compounds; for the purposes of discussion, these two types will be treated separately, although it is obvious that certain features may be common. The treatment will not be as extensive as the subject of azo compounds warrants, since the excellent book of Zollinger[1] and other less complete reviews are available.[2,3,4]

4-2. AROMATIC AZO COMPOUNDS

Only compounds having both aromatic substituents (I, R = R' = aryl) will be considered in this section; all others will be discussed under aliphatic azo compounds.

Preparation

More than a century ago, Griess discovered that aromatic diazonium salts (Chapter 5) will couple with activated aromatic compounds (coupling component) to give highly colored compounds, which have become known as "azo dyes." These synthetic dyes have found extensive use as colorants and have assumed a growing importance in this field:

$$+ \text{HCl} \quad (4\text{–}1)$$

It is not surprising that, although limited to activated aromatic compounds (amines, phenols) the *diazo coupling reaction* is by far the most widely used method for the synthesis of aromatic azo compounds. Excellent reviews[1,4,5] of this reaction are available and no discussion is necessary. Suffice it to mention that attack takes place almost exclusively *para* to the activating group, and *ortho* if the *para* position is blocked. Coupling is essentially instantaneous. Active methylene groups can also react with diazonium salts and will be discussed in Chapter 5.

Despite the popularity and the practicability of the coupling reaction, numerous other methods for the synthesis of aromatic azo compounds have been devised to supplement it where it is not applicable. For example, the reduction of aromatic nitro, nitroso, and azoxy compounds gives azo compounds by a number of procedures:

$$2 \text{ Ar}\!-\!\text{NO}_2 \xrightarrow{\text{reduction}} \text{Ar}\!-\!\text{N}\!=\!\text{N}\!-\!\text{Ar} \qquad (4\text{–}2)$$

The oxidation of aromatic amines or their condensation with aromatic nitroso compounds also yields aromatic azo compounds. Condensation with quinones or oxidation of aromatic hydrazines,

$$2 \text{ ArNH}_2 \xrightarrow{\text{oxidation}} \text{Ar}\!-\!\text{N}\!=\!\text{N}\!-\!\text{Ar} \leftarrow \text{Ar}\!-\!\text{N}\!=\!\text{O} + \text{H}_2\text{N}\!-\!\text{Ar} \quad (4\text{–}3)$$

can also give azo compounds as well as the decomposition of diazonium salts or the rearrangement of aromatic triazenes (Fischer-Hepp type rearrangement). Azoxy compounds undergo the Wallach rearrangement with formation of hydroxy azo compounds.

A mechanistically interesting though not useful method is the disproportionation of hydrazo compounds. It has been demonstrated that hydrazobenzene can be pyrolyzed to aniline and azobenzene without cleavage of the N—N bond of the resulting azobenzene; i.e., hydrazobenzene is oxidized to the azo compound.

Reactions

Under the influence of light, *trans* azo compounds, the stable form, can be isomerized to the *cis* isomers. The azo bond is very stable to heat and is not affected by many reagents. There has been no systematic investigations of the reactions of azo compounds. As would be expected, the azo group is an *o,p*-director in electrophilic substitution reactions. They can be reduced to the corresponding hydrazo compounds, and on further reduction the N—N bond will be cleaved to give amines. Azoxy compounds are formed on oxidation of azo compounds.

Methyl-substituted aromatic compounds will cleave azo compounds at high temperature to give a Schiff base and an amine, presumably via an addition product:

$$\phi—N{=}N—\phi + \phi CH_3 \xrightarrow{\Delta} \left[\begin{array}{c} \phi—N—NH\phi \\ | \\ CH_2\phi \end{array} \right]$$

$$\longrightarrow \phi—N{=}CH—\phi + \phi NH_2 \qquad (4\text{-}4)$$

The addition product of arylsulfinic acids across the —N=N— bond can be isolated. Alkali metals give the disalts of the hydrazo compounds; *cis*-azobenzene adds diphenylketene (4–5):

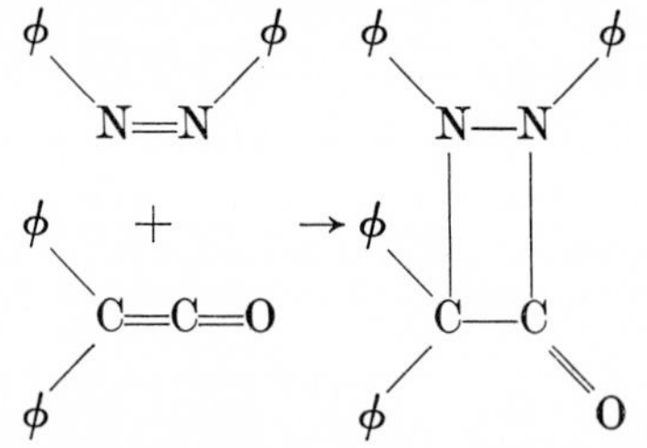

$$(4\text{-}5)$$

It might be interesting to mention the formation of benzo-[c]-cinnoline (II) from the irradiation of *cis*-azobenzene:

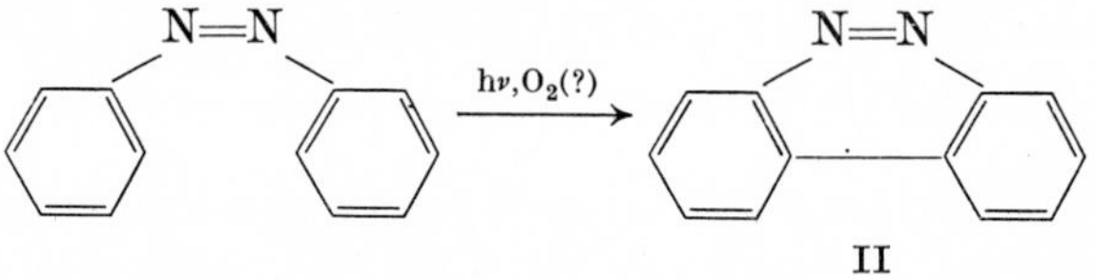

$$(4\text{-}6)$$

II

4–3. ALIPHATIC AZO COMPOUNDS

In this section, all non-aromatic (see definition) azo compounds will be discussed, including purely aliphatic (I, R = R′ = alkyl), "mixed" aliphatic aromatic (I, R = aryl, R′ = alkyl). Esters and amides of acyl azo compounds will be discussed in Chapter 6.

Preparation

The most important method for the synthesis of aliphatic azo compounds consists in the oxidation of the corresponding hydrazines:

$$R—NH—NH—R' \xrightarrow{\text{oxidation}} R—N{=}N—R' \qquad (4\text{-}7)$$

A wide range of oxidizing agents has been utilized for this purpose, the most popular one being mercuric oxide. However, there are other routes that can lead to the azo group; for example, the reaction of aromatic diazonium salts with cyanide or benzenesulfinate ions gives the azo compounds (see Chapter 5):

$$\phi—\overset{+}{N}{\equiv}N\ Cl^- + X^- \rightarrow \phi—N{=}N—X \tag{4-8}$$

where $X = -CN$, $-SO_2\phi$, etc. It is sometimes possible to oxidize N-halo-amines to the corresponding azo compounds. It is not clear whether the reaction proceeds via the "nitrene" or via a displacement-elimination mechanism. "Mixed" aliphatic aromatic azo compounds can be obtained by the reaction of diazonium salts with a zinc alkyl. This achieves the same result as the diazonium coupling reaction with carbanions (Chapter 5) although the mechanism may not be the same:

$$R—ZnCl + \phi—\overset{+}{N}{\equiv}N\ Cl^- \rightarrow R—N{=}N—\phi + ZnCl_2 \tag{4-9}$$

Benzig[6] has extended and studied the chlorination of ketazines, first reported by Goldschmidt, which yields α,α'-bis-chloro azo compounds. From these bis-chloro compounds, numerous α,α'-disubstituted azo compounds can be obtained:

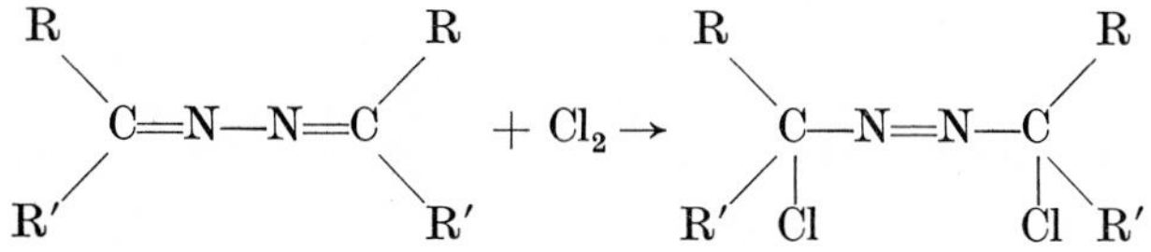

$$\tag{4-10}$$

Somewhat similar is the oxidation of hydrazones to α-acetoxyazo compounds (azo acetates) with lead tetraacetate. This reaction first reported by Iffland, Salisbury, and Schafer[7] has been extended to 2-pyrazolines by Freeman:[8]

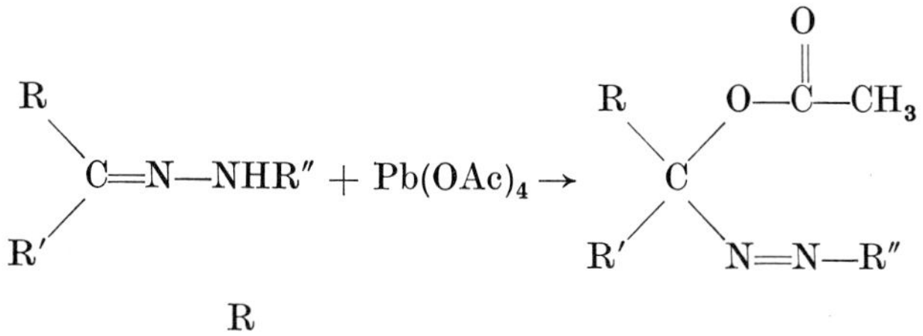

$$\tag{4-11}$$

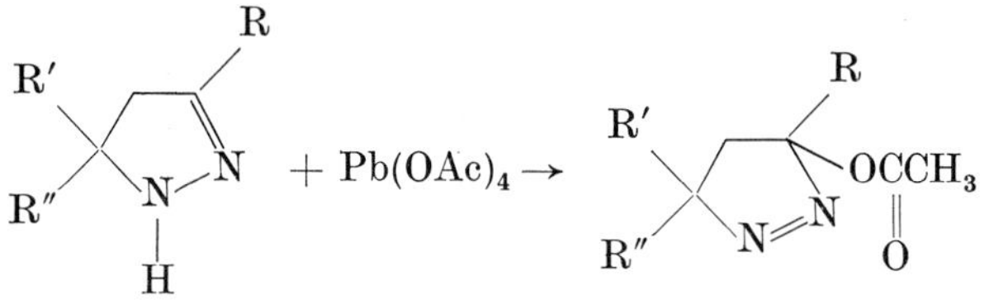

$$\tag{4-12}$$

Perfluoro azoalkanes have been synthesized by the fluorination of nitriles[9] and decompose both thermally and photolytically to give perfluoroalkyl radicals.[9,10]

The reaction of diazoalkanes with olefins (Chapter 5) has been shown to give five-membered ring azo compounds (1-pyrazolines), even when the formation of the more stable hydrazones is favored:[11,23a,b]

$$ArCH{=}CH_2 + Ar\overset{-}{C}H{-}N{\overset{+}{=}}N \rightarrow Ar{-}HC\underset{N=N}{\overset{CH_2}{\diagup\diagdown}}CH{-}Ar \quad (4\text{--}13)$$

A recent paper[12] reported the direct reduction of azine III to the azo compound IV. The reaction of argentic fluoride with cyanogen gives a perfluoro compound for which a four-membered ring structure containing the azo linkage has been assigned:[13]

$$(4\text{--}14a)$$

It thermally decomposes to give tetrafluoroethylene:

$$AgF + (CN)_2 \longrightarrow F{-}\underset{N=N}{\overset{F\quad F}{|{-}{-}|}}{-}F \xrightarrow{150°C} F_2C{=}CF_2 + N_2 \quad (4\text{--}14b)$$

The preparation and the reactions of diazirine (three-membered ring azo compounds) are deferred until Chapter 5.

Reactions

Contrary to their aromatic counterparts, most aliphatic azo compounds are relatively unstable, undergoing homolytic fission under the influence of heat or light. The lability of aliphatic azo compounds will obviously depend on the nature of the substituents; "mixed" aralkyl azo compounds are more stable, as expected. Even azomethane ($CH_3{-}N{=}N{-}CH_3$), a gas, does not decompose appreciably below 200°C. However, when α-substitutents capable of stabilizing the resulting free radicals are introduced, homolytic fission occurs more readily. Furthermore, steric factors will play a determining role, as will be seen in the case of cyclic and hindered azo compounds.

Besides the propensity of aliphatic azo compounds for homolytic decomposition, their isomerization to the hydrazones (particularly when such isomerization results in the formation of a conjugated system) is often an annoying factor to be contended with in the cases where this is possible (presence of α-hydrogen). This problem has been recently investigated and discussed by O'Connor.[14] The reactions of azodiacyl with dienes (Diels-Alder) and other compounds will be dealt with in Chapter 6.

Homolytic Decomposition. By far the most important reaction of aliphatic azo compounds is their decomposition to nitrogen and free radicals under the influence of heat or light. Interest in the mechanism of this decomposition, both practical and theoretical, was revived by the classical investigations of Lewis[15a] and Overberger[15b] on the kinetics of the decomposition of azobisisobutyronitrile and its suitability as a polymerization initiator.

Although the problem of whether the two carbon-nitrogen bonds are ruptured simultaneously has been difficult to resolve, it has now been established that both C—N bonds contribute to the rate-determining step. This is in accordance with the initial suggestions of Ramsperger,[16a] who

TABLE 4–I

Decomposition of Aralkyl Azo Compounds

Compound	A	B	D	E	F	G	Rate (sec.$^{-1}$ × 10^4) t, 120°C	E_a	ΔS
I	CH_3	ϕ	H	CH_3	H	CH_3	0.132	36.5	9.3
II	CH_3	ϕ	CH_3	CH_3	H	CH_3	1.06	36.7	14
III	C_2H_5	ϕ	C_2H_5	C_2H_5	H	C_2H_5	0.78	39.0	19
IV	CH_3	ϕ	i-C_4H_9	CH_3	H	i-C_4H_9	8.51	35.2	15
V	CH_3	ϕ	H	CH_3	ϕ	H	4.85	32.6	7
VI	C_2H_5	ϕ	H	C_2H_5	ϕ	H	2.06	32.3	—
VII	i-C_4H_9	ϕ	H	i-C_4H_9	ϕ	H	7.11	33.3	9
VIII	H	ϕ	H	H	ϕ	H	0.045	35.0	5
IX	CH_3	H	CH_3	CH_3	H	CH_3	0.00001	40.9	1

$$\begin{array}{ccc} A & & E \\ | & & | \\ B-C-N{=}N-C-F \\ | & & | \\ D & & G \end{array}$$

studied the vapor-phase decomposition of a series of aliphatic azoalkanes. Cohen and Wang[16b] have compared the decomposition rate of azomethane, azo-bis-isopropane, 1-azo-bis-1-phenylethane and azo-bis-diphenylmethane, and have shown that replacement of the α-hydrogens by methyl or phenyl substituents had an approximately additive effect on the decrease in activation energy. This observation, in conjunction with an additional comparison of phenylazodiphenylmethane with phenylazotriphenylmethane and azo-bis-diphenylmethane, led them to conclude that this effect was due largely to resonance stabilization of the radicals formed by the decomposition.

Further support for the conclusion that both radicals attached to the azo linkage participate in the rate-determining step can be derived from the data[16c] in Table 4–1. From a comparison of compounds, I, V, and IX, it can be seen that replacement of a methyl group in IX by a phenyl (I) has resulted in a decrease of approximately 4 kcal. in the E_a; subsequent replacement of a pair of methyls in IX by a pair of phenyls, V, produced a decrease of 8 kcal., and additive effect as previously discussed. The increase in reactivity was less predictable since it was dependent on both the E_a and ΔS, but the magnitude of the enhancement in both cases was much greater than the statistical factor of 2 expected if a stepwise decomposition occurred. Both the additive effect and the rate enhancement were consistent with the theory that both radicals contribute to the rate-determining step.

This interpretation has been further substantiated by the magnitude of the secondary α-deuterium isotope effect found for azo-bis-α-phenylethane-α,α'-d$_2$.[16d] The observed effect, $k_H/k_D = 1.27$ was approximately twice as large as those encountered in other "unimolecular" reactions indicating that the two C—N bonds are breaking simultaneously in the transition state of the rate-controlling step. Therefore, the mechanism of decomposition can be pictured as

$$
\begin{array}{ccc}
\underset{\phi}{\overset{CH_3}{H-C-}}N=N\underset{\phi}{\overset{CH_3}{-C-H}} & \xrightarrow{\text{slow}} & \left[\underset{\phi}{\overset{CH_3}{H-C}}\cdots N=N\cdots\underset{\phi}{\overset{CH_3}{C-H}}\right]
\end{array}
$$

(4–15)

$$
\text{2,3-diphenylbutane} \longleftarrow 2\ \underset{H}{\overset{CH_3}{\phi-C\cdot}}\ +\ N_2\,.
$$

As Cohen and Wang predicted, the predominant factor governing the stability of the aliphatic azo compounds is the resonance stability of the radical fragments formed on decomposition. Thus the relative decomposition rates of azo compounds containing the following group of substituents would be in the order:

$$CH_3 < i\text{-}C_3H_7 < \phi CH_2 < \phi CHCH_3 < (CH_3)_2C\text{—}CN \simeq$$
$$(CH_3)_2\text{—}C\text{—}COOCH_3 < \phi_2CH < \phi_3C.$$

The steric effect on the decomposition rate has been demonstrated by Overberger and co-workers[17] utilizing a series of azonitriles with the structure

$$
\underset{CN}{\overset{}{R-C}}\underset{}{\overset{R'\ N}{\diagup\ \diagdown}}\underset{R'}{\overset{\overset{CN}{|}}{C-R}}\quad N
$$

where R and R' are alkyl substituents. When R and R' were methyl, ethyl, isopropyl, or t-butyl, similar rates were observed, indicating that there was probably no change in the transition state. However, when branching was introduced on the carbon β- to the azo linkage, a striking rate enhancement was observed. These results, coupled with similar data obtained by Hyson et al.[18] on the carbamylazonitriles ($RR'(CN)C$—N=N—$CONH_2$), where there was no possibility of steric interaction between the two halves of the molecule, indicated that the steric effect was probably due to "B" strain, that is, the relief of strain on the α-carbon in going from the tetrahedral to the planar configuration in the transition state. This effect is readily observable in Table 4–1 when one considers the progression of increased β-substitution in compounds II and IV.

TABLE 4–2

Decomposition Rates of Azonitriles from Cycloalkanones

Compound	Rate (sec.$^{-1} \times 10^4$) t, 80.0°C	E_a	ΔS
X, $n = 1$	0.00173	32.1	1.3
X, $n = 2$	0.726	33.8	18.9
X, $n = 3$	0.063	35.4	17.8
X, $n = 4$	12.22	27.5	6.1
X, $n = 5$	83.5	25.9	5.9
X, $n = 7$	18.12	28.0	8.5

X

Since the decomposition is relatively insensitive to solvent effects,[22] it provided an elegant procedure for demonstrations of "I" strain (ring strain) in a free radical reaction.[19] Table 4–2 summarizes the results obtained from a series of cycloalkylazonitriles. The enhanced rate of decomposition of compound X, $n = 2$ over X, $n = 3$ was indicative of the driving force obtained by the release of ring strain in the transition state of the cyclopentyl compound. Similarly, the decomposition rates of the larger ring compounds were consistent with the "I"-strain suggestion of H. C. Brown.

An analogous study was conducted on a series of methyl cycloalkylazonitriles,[20] and no significant change in rate was observed for the different-sized rings except for the cyclopropyl ring. When 2,2'-azo-bis-2-cyclopropylpropionitrile was decomposed, a twentyfold increase in rate was found, which was interpreted as an example of radical stabilization via hyperconjugation in the cyclopropyl ring.

Generally, the products from these decompositions are those expected from a coupling reaction of the two radicals formed or by the abstraction of hydrogen from a solvent molecule. Recently the isolation[21] of dimethyl-N-(2-cyano-2-propyl)-ketenimine (V) confirmed an earlier suggestion that this was an intermediate in the product formation. As shown below, the ketenimine was formed after the rate-determining step involving the nitrogen evolution had occurred and thus would not affect the first-order rate constants previously discussed:

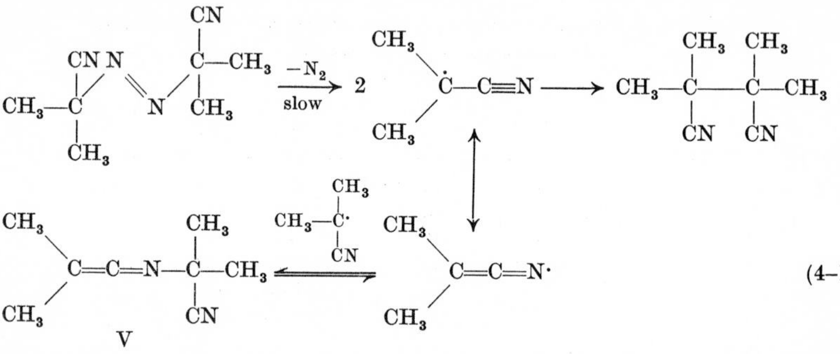

$$(4\text{--}16)$$

A significance of this intermediate was demonstrated by a comparison of the initiation efficiencies for styrene polymerization between the parent azo compound and its corresponding ketenimine. The ketenimine was less efficient, indicating that the reduced efficiency of azo-bis-isobutyronitrile may well be due to this factor rather than to a non-radical cyclic mechanism (4–17) as previously proposed:

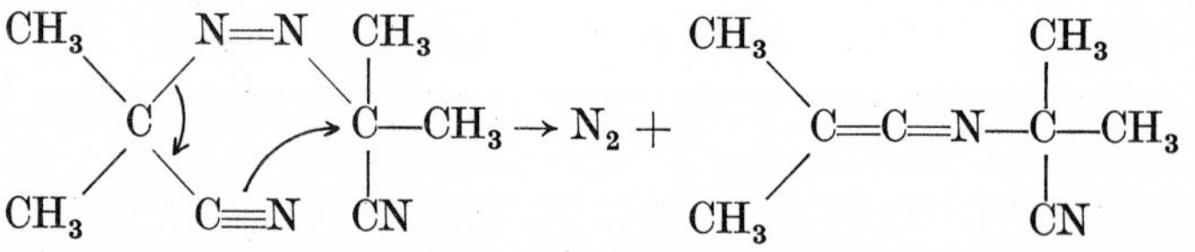

$$(4\text{--}17)$$

The cyclic mechanism has been untenable because only the *trans* configuration was known for linear azo linkages, and the formation of a six-membered ring containing a *trans* azo bond was difficult to imagine.

The influence of steric factors was demonstrated by the effect of the incorporation of the azo linkage into a cyclic structure (VI). This forces the azo bond into a *cis*-configuration. The pertinent data given in Table 4–3 speak eloquently. Several other features can be noted. The remarkably low activation energy of the five-membered ring compound (VI, $n = 1$) confirms the quasiplanar configuration of the ring as well as the strain associated with it.[23] The anomalously slow rate of decomposition of the eight-membered ring is understandable in terms of the difficulties of the C—N=N—C system to become coplanar with α-substituents.[26,27] In compounds of type VII, the azo bond can assume a *trans*-configuration, and therefore the rate is essentially the same as that of azo-bis-1-phenylpropane.

The thermal decomposition of the cyclic azo compounds of type VI gave interesting results. The seven- and eight-membered ring homologues ($n = 3, 4$), presumably one isomer in each case, led to a mixture of *cis*- and

TABLE 4–3

Data on the Decomposition of Cyclic Azo Compounds

Compound	Rate (sec.$^{-1}$, 80°C)	Relative Rate	E_a (kcal./mole)	Reference
φ, C₂H₅ CH—N=N—CH C₂H₅, φ	1.9×10^{-6}	1	36.7	26
VI, $n = 1$	1.2×10^{-3}	631	17.9	23b
VI, $n = 2$	6.0×10^{-4}	375	—	24
VI, $n = 3$	4.3×10^{-4}	268	29.7	25
VII, $n = 4$	3.5×10^{-8}	0.02	36.7	26

VI   VII

trans-1,2-diphenylcycloalkanes and the corresponding olefins, while the six-membered ring ($n = 2$) yielded styrene. In contrast, the *trans* five-membered ring ($n = 1$) gave *trans*-1,2-diphenylcyclopropane as the major product of decomposition. This would suggest that the biradical intermediates formed from the seven- and eight-membered rings were free and stable enough to "racemize" before coupling, while bond formation took place very fast in the case of the five-membered ring compound;[23a] it was recently shown[23b] that *cis*-3,5-dianisyl-1-pyrazoline gave a mixture of the corresponding *cis*- and *trans*-cyclopropanes.

The greater lability of 9-phenylfluorenylazobenzenes over the corresponding triphenylmethylazobenzenes has been attributed to the greater stabilization of the resulting free radicals.[28] The effect of strain, already apparent from Table 4–3 (rate decrease in VI as n varies from 1 to 4) was further demonstrated by the comparative rates of decomposition of VIII and

IX; it was found[29] that VIII decomposed 380 times faster than IX and its activation energy was some 7 kcal./mole lower, no kinetic study for the interesting quadracyclic azo compound X was reported:[30a]

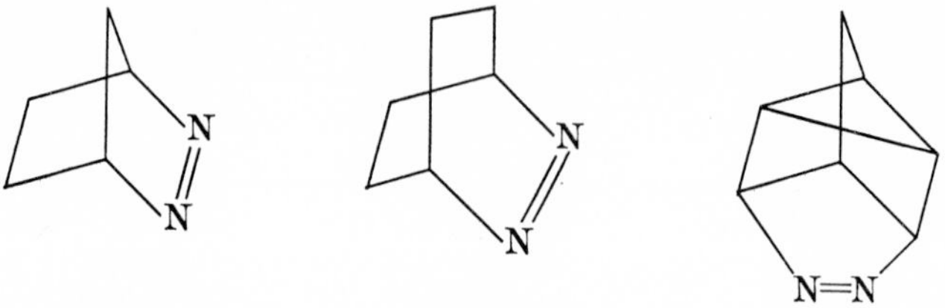

VIII   IX   X

Berson and co-workers[30b] have recently shown that the same products (qualitatively) are formed from compounds XI and XII:

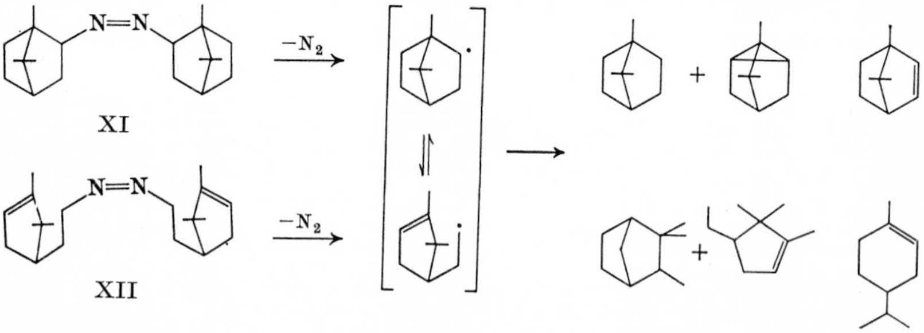

Depending on the nature and the reactivity of the free radicals formed, they will either react with the solvent (very reactive radicals such as $CH_3\cdot$) or with themselves (dimerization) or attack a reactive substrate. The inability of radical scavengers to trap certain reactive free radicals has led to the assumption that the "cage effect"[31] was operating; the free radicals, surrounded by the solvent molecules are unable to diffuse through the so-called "solvent cage." This has been amply demonstrated by Hammond[32] and others.[33]

Some azoalkanes form stable addition compounds with cupric salts.[34]

REFERENCES

General

H. ZOLLINGER, *Diazo and Azo Chemistry: Aliphatic and Aromatic Compounds*, Interscience Publishers, Inc., New York, 1961.

C. G. OVERBERGER, New reactions of 1,1- and 1,2-disubstituted hydrazines, *Record Chem. Prog.*, **21**, 21 (1960).

Text

1. H. ZOLLINGER, *Diazo and Azo Chemistry: Aliphatic and Aromatic Compounds*, Interscience Publishers, Inc., New York, 1961.

2. C. G. OVERBERGER, *Record Chem. Progr.*, **21**, 21 (1960).

3. A. GUILLEMONAT and A. GISLON, in V. GRIGNARD (ed.), *Traité de Chimie Organique*, vol. 15, Masson et Cie, Paris, 1948, p. 257.

4. E. H. RODD, *Chemistry of Carbon Compounds*, vol. 3-A, Elsevier Publishing Company, New York, 1954, p. 319.

5. K. H. SAUNDERS, *The Aromatic Diazo Compounds*, Longmans, Green and Co., London, 1949.

6. E. BENZIG, *Chimia*, **13**, 89 (1959); *Angew.Chem.*, **72**, 571 (1960); and later papers.

7. D. C. IFFLAND, L. SALISBURY, and W. R. SCHAFER, *J. Am. Chem. Soc.*, **83**, 747 (1961).

8. J. P. FREEMAN, *J. Org. Chem.*, **28**, 885 (1963).

9. J. A. YOUNG, W. S. DURRELL, and R. D. DRESDNER, *J. Am. Chem. Soc.*, **82**, 4553 (1960); W. J. CHAMBERS, C. W. TULLOCK, and D. D. COFFMAN, *ibid.*, **84**, 2337 (1962); J. H. ATTAWAY, R. H. GROTH, and L. A. BIGELOW, *ibid.*, **81**, 3599 (1959).

10. J. A. YOUNG and R. D. DRESDNER, *J. Org. Chem.*, **28**, 833 (1963).

11. C. G. OVERBERGER and J-P. ANSELME, *J. Am. Chem. Soc.*, **84**, 869 (1962).

12. J. KOSSANYI, *Compt. Rend.*, **257**, 929 (1963); however, see *Bull. Soc. Chim. France*, **1965**, 722.

13. H. J. EMELEUS and G. L. HURST, *J. Chem. Soc.*, 3276 (1962).

14. R. O'CONNOR, *J. Org. Chem.*, **26**, 4375 (1961); R. O'CONNOR and W. ROSENBROOK, *J. Am. Chem. Soc.*, **26**, 5208 (1961).

15. (a) F. M. LEWIS and M. S. MATHESON, *J. Am. Chem. Soc.*, **71**, 747 (1949).
    (b) C. G. OVERBERGER, M. T. O'SHAUGHNESSY, and H. SHALIT, *J. Am. Chem. Soc.*, **71**, 2661 (1949).

16. (a) H. C. RAMSPERGER, *J. Am. Chem. Soc.*, **51**, 2141 (1929).
    (b) S. G. COHEN and C. H. WANG, *J. Am. Chem. Soc.*, **77**, 2457 (1955); **75**, 5504 (1953).
    (c) C. G. OVERBERGER and A. V. DiGIULIO, *J. Am. Chem. Soc.*, **81**, 2154 (1959).
    (d) S. SELTZER, *J. Am. Chem. Soc.*, **85**, 14 (1963).

17. C. G. OVERBERGER *et al.*, *J. Am. Chem. Soc.*, **73**, 2618, 4880, 4883 (1951); **76**, 6185 (1954).

18. A. M. HYSON *et al.*, Abstracts of the 129th Meeting of the American Chemical Society, Dallas, Tex., April 8 to 13, 1956, p. 6R.

19. C. G. OVERBERGER *et al.*, *J. Am. Chem. Soc.*, **75**, 2078 (1953).

20. (a) C. G. OVERBERGER and A. LEBOVITS, *J. Am. Chem. Soc.* **76**, 2722 (1954).
    (b) C. G. OVERBERGER, M. TOBKES, and A. ZWEIG, *J. Org. Chem.*, **28**, 620 (1963).

21. M. TALAT-ERBEN and S. BYWATER, *J. Am. Chem. Soc.*, **77**, 3710, 3712 (1955); G. S. HAMMOND *et al.*, *ibid.*, **81**, 4878 (1959); **82**, 5386, 5394 (1960).

22. J. E. LEFFLER and R. A. HUBBARD, *J. Org. Chem.*, **19**, 1089 (1954); J. G. ADLER and J. E. LEFFLER, *J. Am. Chem. Soc.*, **76**, 1425 (1954); R. C. PETERSON, J. H. MARKGRAF, and S. D. ROSS, *ibid.*, **83**, 3819 (1961).

23. (a) C. G. OVERBERGER and J-P. ANSELME, *J. Am. Chem. Soc.*, **86**, 658 (1964).
    (b) C. G. OVERBERGER, N. WEINSHENKER, and J-P. ANSELME, *J. Am. Chem. Soc.*, **86**, 5364 (1964); **87**, 4119 (1965).

24. S. G. COHEN, S. HSIAO, E. SAKLAD, and C. H. WANG, *J. Am. Chem. Soc.*, **79**, 4400 (1957).

25. C. G. OVERBERGER and J. G. LOMBARDINO, *J. Am. Chem. Soc.*, **80**, 2317 (1958).

26. C. G. OVERBERGER and I. TASHLICK, *J. Am. Chem. Soc.*, **81**, 217 (1959).

27. C. G. OVERBERGER, J-P. ANSELME, and J. R. HALL, *J. Am. Chem. Soc.*, **85**, 2752 (1963).

28. S. G. COHEN, F. COHEN, and C. H. WANG, *J. Org. Chem.*, **28**, 1479 (1963).

29. S. G. COHEN and R. ZAND, *J. Am. Chem. Soc.*, **84**, 586 (1962).

30. (a) R. M. MORIARTY, *J. Org. Chem.*, **28**, 2385 (1963).
     (b) J. A. BERSON, C. J. OLSEN, and J. S. WALIA, *J. Am. Chem. Soc.*, **84**, 3337 (1962).

31. J. FRANK and E. RABINOVITCH, *Trans. Faraday Soc.*, **30**, 120 (1934).

32. G. S. HAMMOND and R. C. NEUMAN, *J. Am. Chem. Soc.*, **85**, 1501 (1963).

33. L. HERK, M. FELD, and M. SZWARC, *J. Am. Chem. Soc.*, **83**, 2998 (1961); R. K. LYON and D. H. LEVY, *ibid.*, **83**, 4290 (1961); S. KODAMA, *Bull. Chem. Soc. Japan*, **35**, 827 (1962).

34. O. DIELS and W. KOLL, *Ann.*, **443**, 262 (1925).

5

Diazo Compounds

5–1. INTRODUCTION

The aliphatic and aromatic diazo compounds contain two nitrogen atoms joined to a single carbon atom. The nature of the carbon to which the diazo group ($-N\overset{+}{=}N$) is bonded distinguishes diazoalkanes (aliphatic) from diazonium salts (aromatic). Thus diazoalkanes (II) have the diazo function attached to a primary or secondary carbon atom, which, by loss of an α-proton, gives a neutral, resonance-stabilized molecule:

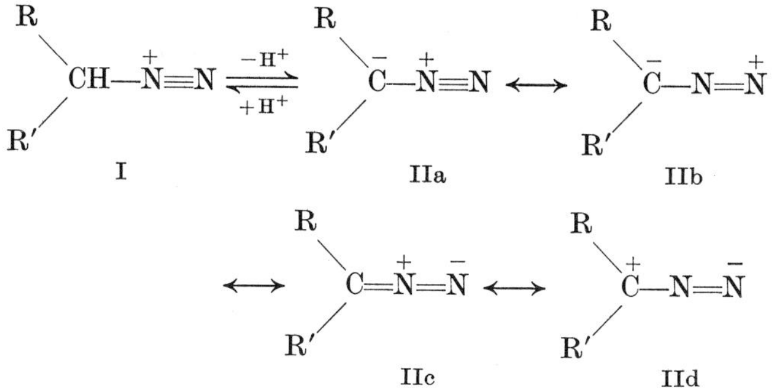

The properties and also the synthesis of diazoalkanes can be understood by this loss of the α-proton, since without this important step compounds of type I would immediately lose nitrogen. Tertiary aliphatic diazo compounds, $R_3C-N\overset{+}{\equiv}N\ X^-$, incapable of such resonance stabilization are not known, although they are believed to be highly reactive intermediates in the reaction of aliphatic amines with nitrous acid. In certain special cases the loss of a proton at a site far removed from the diazo group can occur, as in the formation of diazooxides (III) and diazoimines (IV):

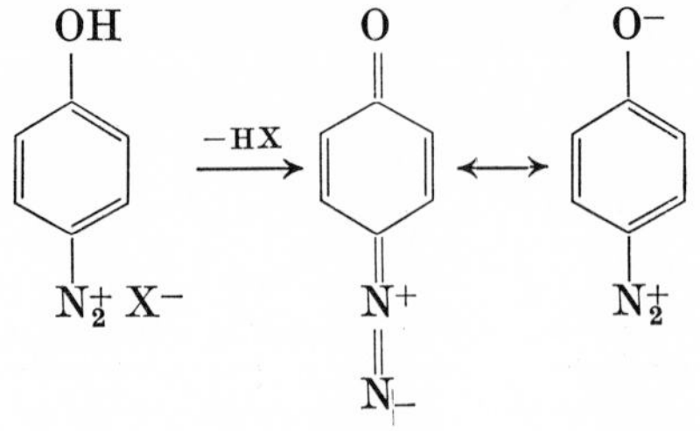

IIIa   IIIb

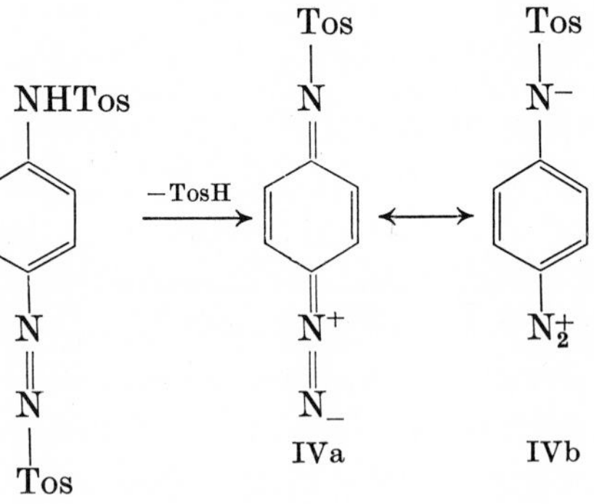

IVa   IVb

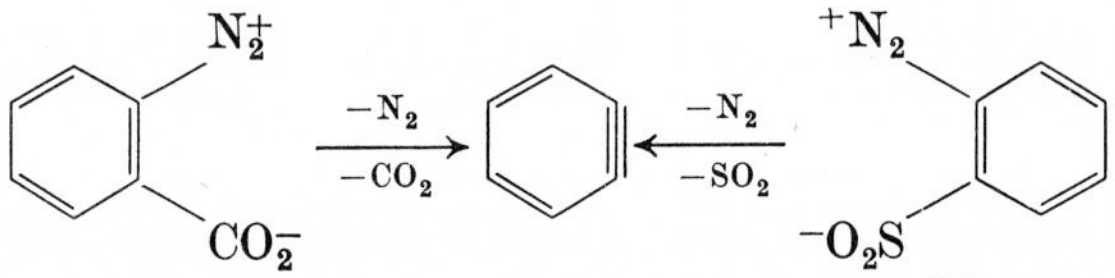

V   VI

o-Diazonium carboxylate (V) and *o*-diazonium sulfinate (VI) have been used to generate benzyne (dehydrobenzene). Addition of even weakly acidic substances to solutions of diazoalkanes generates I, which immediately loses nitrogen* (see "Reactions").

The stability of diazoalkanes increases when R and R′ are capable of resonance interaction with the α-carbon. As R and R′ are varied from hydrogen and alkyl groups to aromatic or carbonyl functions (VII), the aliphatic diazo compounds become more stable. The case of the extremely stable diazocyclopentadiene (VIII) is especially interesting since the negative charge is taken up in the formation of the 6 π-electrons system of the ring.

---

* Reimlinger has recently reported (*Angew. Chem.* **75**, 788 (1963)) the preparation of a stable non-aromatic diazonium salt; see also K. Bott, *ibid.*, **76**, 992 (1964).

Bis-(trifluoromethyl) diazomethane is stable to acids:

VII   VIII

While many diazocarbonyl compounds are stable at room temperature and may be handled without special precautions, it should be noted that some aromatic diazooxides are *extremely* explosive compounds which usually cannot be isolated. The simple aliphatic diazo compounds are difficult and dangerous to isolate, on account of their toxic and explosive properties. They are usually prepared at low temperatures in an inert solvent and used immediately to avoid any handling or storage problems.

Diazonium salts (IX) are *ionic* compounds in which the diazo group is bonded to an aromatic residue. Resonance interaction of the diazo group with the aromatic residue discourages to some extent the tendency for the loss of nitrogen. Nonetheless, most diazonium salts can exist only at low temperatures and *explosive* decomposition occurs with evolution of nitrogen when they are warmed slightly:

IXa   IXb   IXc

Several good reviews on the chemistry of diazo compounds[1] are available and should be consulted for more extensive coverage. The general reactions and preparations of diazo compounds will be mentioned briefly, and the more unusual and interesting features will be emphasized.

5–2. AROMATIC DIAZONIUM SALTS

Structure

The importance of the diazonium salts in the dye industry, as well as their interesting and varied reactions, has encouraged a great deal of investigation in this field. Saunders[1] and, more recently, Zollinger[1b] have covered thoroughly the chemistry of diazonium salts and should be referred to for more detailed discussions. However, the structure of diazonium salts is interesting and controversial enough to warrant a few words on the present views concerning this problem.

It is well established now that the diazonium salts, as their nomenclature indicates, are ionic compounds, with the positive charge residing mainly on the two nitrogen atoms.   However, the participation of the aromatic residue in the stabilization of diazonium salts spreads the positive charge on the ring, thus reducing to some extent the tendency to lose elemental nitrogen. Furthermore, it has been shown that the two nitrogen atoms are *not* equivalent, thus ruling out the cyclic structure A, although recent evidence[2] indicates that a symmetrical intermediate is involved during the hydrolysis of benzene diazonium fluoroborate.   This permits the nitrogen atoms to lose their identity:

A

When an aqueous solution of a diazonium salt is treated slowly with a solution of sodium hydroxide, the diazonium cation is not affected; only the nature of the anion is changed, and soon, as more of the solution of sodium hydroxide is added, the formation of the diazohydroxide takes place (5–1). This intermediate is very short-lived and is immediately converted to the *syn*-diazotate as more of the basic solution is added (5–2). This *syn*-diazotate is very reactive and rearranges to the more stable *anti*-diazotate (5–3):

$$Ar{-}N_2^+ + OH^- \overset{\text{slow}}{\rightleftharpoons} syn\text{-}ArN{=}N{-}OH \qquad (5\text{--}1)$$

$$syn\text{-}Ar{-}N{=}N{-}OH + OH^- \overset{\text{fast}}{\rightleftharpoons} syn\text{-}Ar{-}N{=}N{-}O^- + H_2O \quad (5\text{--}2)$$

$$syn\text{-}Ar{-}N{=}N{-}O^- \overset{\text{slow}}{\rightleftharpoons} anti\text{-}Ar{-}N{=}N{-}O^- \qquad (5\text{--}3)$$

Thus, if to 1 mole of a diazonium salt 1 mole of base is added, only a half is converted to the diazotate, and therefore diazonium salts behave like dibasic acids.   It has been possible to isolate the "diazoanhydrides" (X) of diazohydroxides:

$$Ar{-}N{=}N{-}O{-}N{=}N{-}Ar$$
X

When diazonium salts are treated with certain anions, the corresponding diazonium compounds are not formed; instead, covalent and water-insoluble materials are isolated.   They are essentially azo compounds (see Chapter 4) and can exist as *cis* and *trans* isomers, the *trans* isomer being the more stable:

cis-phenylazocyanide   *trans*-phenylazocyanide

Preparation

Although the preparation of diazonium salts may be accomplished by several methods (see Zollinger and Rodd), only two procedures have found wide application. The most general consists in the reaction of aromatic amines with sodium nitrite in the presence of an excess of mineral acid. In most cases, good yields of the diazonium salts are obtained:

$$ArNH_2 + 2\ HX + NaNO_2 \rightarrow ArN_2^+\ X^- + NaX + 2\ H_2O \qquad (5\text{--}4)$$

Careful control of the temperature during the diazotization (at or near 0°C) is of capital importance for both successful and safe completion of the reaction. Slightly higher temperatures may be used for the more stable ones such as p-nitrobenzene and naphthyldiazonium chlorides.

When the diazonium salts are required in the pure state, a useful preparative method utilizes the reaction of an alkyl nitrite and the amine in an organic solvent. Excellent yields of the diazonium salt are obtained by the addition of ether. A recent procedure using nitrosyl sulfuric acid in acetic acid gives the pure diazonium bisulfate.[3]

The direct introduction of the diazonium group reported by Tedder is restricted to phenols and dialkylanilines:

$$\langle\ \rangle\text{---OH} + 2\ HONO + H_3O^+ \rightarrow {}^+N_2\text{---}\langle\ \rangle\text{---OH} \qquad (5\text{--}4a)$$

Reactions

Because of the positive charge on these compounds, nucleophilic attack by various species constitutes the main class of reactions of diazonium salts. They can be divided into two general classes: (a) nucleophilic attack at the terminal nitrogen atom of the diazonium group *without loss of nitrogen*, (b) nucleophilic attack at α-carbon (adjacent to the —N=N⁺ group) *with loss of nitrogen*,

$$ArN\overset{+}{=}N\ Cl^- + BH \rightarrow Ar\text{---}N\!=\!N\text{---}B + HCl \qquad (5\text{--}5)$$

$$ArN\overset{+}{=}N\ Cl^- + BH \rightarrow Ar\text{---}B + N_2 + HCl \qquad (5\text{--}6)$$

In certain cases where the diazo group can withstand the conditions, nuclear substitution or exchange may occur without loss of nitrogen. Various reactions of lesser importance are also possible.

Reactions Without Loss of Nitrogen. Various nucleophiles attack diazonium salts at the terminal nitrogen atom to give arylazo compounds.

In this manner, arylazocyanides (diazocyanides), arylazosulfonates (diazosulfonates), and numerous similar compounds have been prepared. One interesting example is the reaction of azide ion with diazonium salts. The intermediate "arylazoazide" cannot be isolated and cyclizes to the reactive pentazole ring.[3b] This in turn loses nitrogen to form the corresponding arylazide:

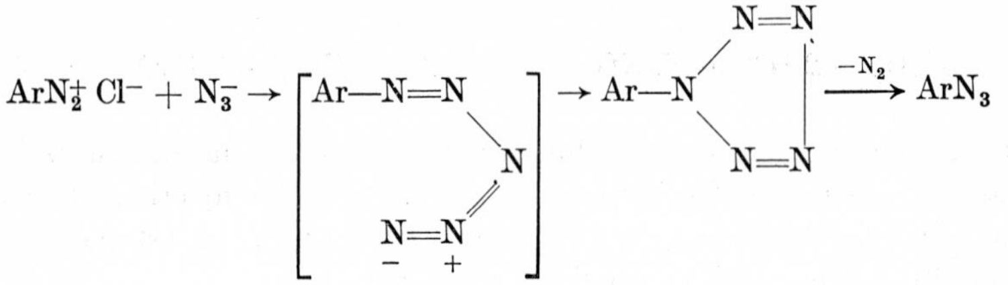

$$\text{ArN}_2^+ \text{ Cl}^- + \text{N}_3^- \rightarrow \left[\begin{array}{c} \text{Ar—N=N} \\ \diagdown \\ \quad\quad \text{N} \\ \diagup\diagup \\ \text{N=N} \\ -\quad + \end{array} \right] \rightarrow \text{Ar—N} \begin{array}{c} \text{N=N} \\ \diagup \quad \diagdown \\ \quad\quad\quad | \\ \diagdown \quad \diagup \\ \text{N=N} \end{array} \xrightarrow{-\text{N}_2} \text{ArN}_3 \quad (5\text{-}7)$$

The importance of the coupling reactions of diazonium salts with activated aromatic compounds to give highly colored dyes needs no emphasis. Several reviews[1] are available. Coupling can also take place with activated methylene groups as in the diazonium coupling reaction[4] (5-8) and the Japp-Klingeman reaction[5] (5-9):

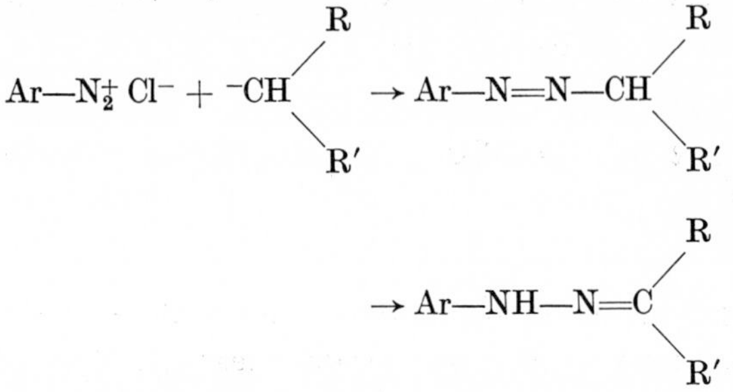

$$\text{Ar—N}_2^+ \text{ Cl}^- + {}^-\text{CH} \begin{array}{c} R \\ \diagup \\ \diagdown \\ R' \end{array} \rightarrow \text{Ar—N=N—CH} \begin{array}{c} R \\ \diagup \\ \diagdown \\ R' \end{array}$$

$$\rightarrow \text{Ar—NH—N=C} \begin{array}{c} R \\ \diagup \\ \diagdown \\ R' \end{array} \quad (5\text{-}8)$$

$$\text{ArN}_2^+ \text{ Cl}^- + \begin{array}{c} R'' \quad H \\ \diagdown \diagup \\ C \\ \diagup \diagdown \\ R' \quad R \end{array} \rightarrow \left[\text{Ar—N=N—CH} \begin{array}{c} R \\ \diagup \\ \diagdown \\ R' \end{array} \right]$$

$$\rightarrow \text{Ar—NH—N=C} \begin{array}{c} R \\ \diagup \\ \diagdown \\ R' \end{array} \quad (5\text{-}9)$$

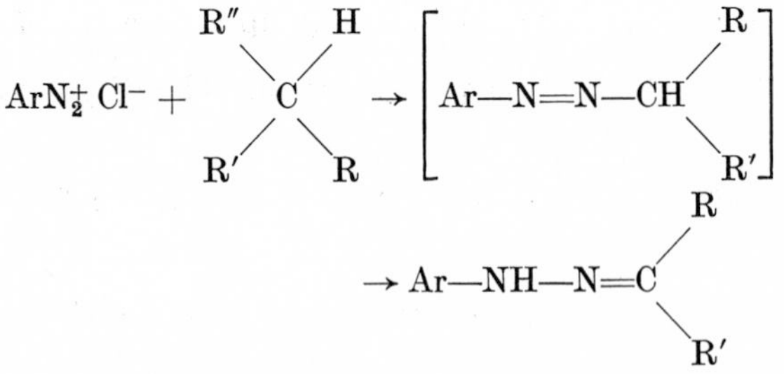

(R' and R'' electron-withdrawing groups)

In certain cases it has been possible to isolate the intermediate azo compound in the Japp-Klingeman reaction.[6] A useful and practical preparation of aldehydes and ketones has made use of the coupling reaction of diazonium salts:[7]

$$R-\underset{\underset{R'}{|}}{\overset{\overset{OH}{|}}{C}}-\overset{}{\bigcirc}-N\overset{CH_3}{\underset{CH_3}{<}} \quad \overset{-O_3S-\bigcirc-\overset{+}{N_2}}{\longrightarrow}$$

$$R-\overset{\overset{O}{\|}}{C}-R' + HO_3S-\bigcirc-N{=}N-\bigcirc-N\overset{CH_3}{\underset{CH_3}{<}} \qquad (5\text{--}10)$$

The reduction of diazonium salts is still the most widely used method for the synthesis of arylhydrazines.

Reactions with Loss of Nitrogen. The widespread use of this type of reaction speaks for its versatility. A number of groups can thus be introduced

TABLE 5–I

Compounds from the Reactions of Diazonium Salts

Compound	Reagents	Name
Aromatic hydrocarbons	H_3PO_2	Deamination reaction[8]
Aromatic halides	HX	Griess reaction
Aromatic halides	CuX	Sandemeyer reaction
Aromatic halides	Cu, HX	Gattermann reaction
Aromatic fluoride	$ArN_2^+ \ BF_4^-$	Schieman reaction[9]
Aromatic arsonic and arsinic acids	Arsenic derivatives	Bart reaction[10]
Biaryls	Base	Gomberg-Bachman reaction[11]

into an aromatic ring by diazotization of the amines followed by the reaction with the appropriate reagents. It is sometimes the only method that will yield the desired product:

$$ArN_2^+ + HB \rightarrow Ar{-}B + N_2 + H^+ \qquad (5\text{--}11)$$

Some reactions in this class are believed to proceed by homolytic cleavage of the aryl nitrogen bond, while under different conditions only an ionic mechanism seems to fit the experimental data. Almost all these reactions are catalyzed by metal salts, especially copper salts. Most organic textbooks describe these reactions, and a schematic description is given in Table 5–1.

The elements of Ar—X can be added across activated olefinic double bonds; this constitutes the Meerwein arylation reaction by means of diazonium salts:[12]

$$ArN_2^+ \ X^- + \underset{/}{\overset{\backslash}{C}}{=}\underset{\backslash}{\overset{/}{C}} \rightarrow Ar{-}\overset{|}{\underset{|}{C}}{-}\overset{|}{\underset{|}{C}}{-}X \qquad (5\text{--}12)$$

Evidence has been presented for both an ionic and a free radical mechanism for the Meerwein reaction. Neither mechanism can explain all the experimental observations, and this has led to a proposed intermediate complex between diazonium salt, olefin, and copper chloride. Such a complex might decompose by an internal one-electron transfer.[12b]

5–3. DIAZOALKANES

Structure

While several excellent discussions[1b,13] on the structure of diazoalkanes (XI) are available, it may be of value to review briefly the general features of the problem.

For a long time, diazoalkanes were represented by the cyclic structure (XII). The controversy between the two schools of thought lasted until it was conclusively shown[1b,13] by physical methods that diazoalkanes have a linear arrangement of the nitrogen atoms and are best described as resonance hybrids[13] of several contribution structures (XIa, b, c, d):

$$\underset{\text{XI}}{\overset{R}{\underset{R'}{>}}C-\overset{-}{N}=\overset{+}{N}} \qquad \underset{\text{XII}}{\overset{R}{\underset{R'}{>}}C\overset{N}{\underset{N}{\big\|}}}$$

$$\underset{\text{XIa}}{\overset{R}{\underset{R'}{>}}C-\overset{-}{N}=\overset{+}{N}} \leftrightarrow \underset{\text{XIb}}{\overset{R}{\underset{R'}{>}}C-\overset{-}{N}\equiv\overset{+}{N}} \leftrightarrow \underset{\text{XIc}}{\overset{R}{\underset{R'}{>}}C=\overset{+}{N}=\overset{-}{N}} \leftrightarrow \underset{\text{XId}}{\overset{R}{\underset{R'}{>}}\overset{+}{C}-\overset{}{N}=\overset{-}{N}}$$

However, the chemical proof of their linear structure did not come until 1960, when Paulsen[14] and Schmitz[15] independently synthesized the first diazirines (XII). Prior to the synthesis of diazirines, which were found to be colorless compared to the highly colored diazoalkanes, it was conceivable that such a cyclic structure could make some contribution, however small, to the resonance hybrid of diazoalkanes. However, it has been conclusively demonstrated[16] that they are different entities. Consequently, the cyclic structure XII is not contributing to the resonance hybrid of diazoalkanes, although differing only in the arrangement of the electrons (see "Tautomerism").

Preparation

Several methods for the synthesis of diazoalkanes are available. Gutsche[17] has discussed their respective merit and has reviewed the literature up to 1954. These methods can be classified under three general headings:

a. *Action of Base on Nitrosoamides.* The action of aqueous base or alkali alkoxides on nitrosoamides gives diazoalkanes according to reaction (5–13):

$$\begin{array}{c}
R \\
\diagdown \\
\qquad CH-N-R'' + base \rightarrow \\
\diagup \qquad | \\
R' \qquad NO
\end{array}
\qquad
\begin{array}{c}
R \\
\diagdown \quad - \quad + \\
\qquad C-N{=}N \\
\diagup \\
R'
\end{array}
\qquad (5\text{–}13)$$

$$(R'' = -CONH_2, -COOC_2H_5, -COR''', -SO_2R''', \overset{\displaystyle NH}{\underset{\displaystyle}{-\overset{\|}{C}-NHNO_2}})$$

b. *Oxidation of Hydrazones.* Hydrazones of aldehydes and ketones can be oxidized to the corresponding diazoalkanes. This method is particularly suited for the preparation of diaryldiazoalkanes:

$$\begin{array}{c}
R \\
\diagdown \\
\qquad C{=}N-NH_2 + HgO \xrightarrow{OH^-} \\
\diagup \\
R'
\end{array}
\qquad
\begin{array}{c}
R \\
\diagdown \quad - \quad + \\
\qquad C-N{=}N \\
\diagup \\
R'
\end{array}
\qquad (5\text{–}14)$$

c. *Action of Nitrous Acid on Amino Compounds.* This procedure is limited to compounds having an amino function adjacent to an electron-withdrawing group:

$$NH_2CH_2COOC_2H_5 \xrightarrow{HONO} \overset{+}{N}{=}N-\overset{-}{C}H-COOC_2H_5 \qquad (5\text{–}15)$$

Several other miscellaneous procedures can yield diazoalkanes. The action of chloroform on hydrazine in the presence of potassium hydroxide and the reaction of N,N-dichloromethylamine with hydroxylamine to give diazomethane are of interest. The base-catalyzed decomposition of azibenzil yields phenyldiazomethane (5–16):

$$\phi-\overset{-}{C}-\overset{\displaystyle O}{\overset{\|}{C}}-\phi \xrightarrow{OH^-} \phi-CHN_2 + \phi COO^- \qquad (5\text{–}16)$$
$$\underset{\underset{\displaystyle N^+}{\diagdown\!\!\!\diagdown}}{\overset{|}{N}}$$

The unique method for the synthesis of diazocyclopentadiene (VIII) and related compounds deserves mention:

$$\text{(cyclopentadiene)}\overset{\ominus}{} + N_3SO_2{-}\phi \rightarrow \text{(ring)} \overset{N{=}N{-}\overset{\ominus}{N}{-}SO_2\phi}{\underset{H}{}} \quad \rightleftharpoons$$

$$\text{(ring)} \overset{\overset{\displaystyle H}{|}}{\underset{\displaystyle \ominus}{N{=}N{\rightleftharpoons}N{-}SO_2\phi}} \rightarrow \text{(ring)}\overset{\ominus}{}{-}N{=}\overset{+}{N} \qquad (5\text{–}17)$$

The instability of nitrosomethylurea and the vesicant properties of nitrosomethylurethane offer certain disadvantages. However, the use of N-nitrosomethyl-p-toluenesulfonamide introduced by de Boer and Backer[18] has the advantage of being easily prepared and extremely stable:

$$R—CH_2—\underset{\underset{NO}{|}}{N}—SO_2—\bigcirc—CH_3 \xrightarrow{base}$$

$$R\overset{-}{C}H\overset{+}{N}_2 + {}^-SO_3—\bigcirc—CH_3 \quad (5\text{-}18)$$

$$(R = H—, \phi—)$$

The base-catalyzed decomposition of p-toluenesulfonylhydrazones (see Chapters 3 and 6) first reported by Bamford and Stevens[19a] has been used to generate diazoalkanes *in situ*, but is not a *general* preparative method as has been claimed recently.[19b] No workable yield of p-methoxyphenyldiazomethane was achieved by this method:[20]

$$\underset{R'}{\overset{R}{\diagdown}}C{=}N{-}\underset{\underset{H}{|}}{N}{-}SO_2R'' \xrightarrow{base} \underset{R'}{\overset{R}{\diagdown}}\overset{-}{C}{-}N{=}\overset{+}{N} + {}^-SO_2R'' \quad (5\text{-}19)$$

The Forster reaction (5-20) of α-oximinoketones to give α-diazoketones has seen some applications, and it has been recently[21] shown that it might be useful as a general method for the synthesis of diazoalkanes:

$$\underset{R'}{\overset{R}{\diagdown}}C{=}N{-}OH + X{-}NH_2 \xrightarrow{base} \underset{R'}{\overset{R}{\diagdown}}\overset{-}{C}{-}N{=}\overset{+}{N} \quad (5\text{-}20)$$

$$(X = —Cl, —OSO_3H)$$

Two new methods for the synthesis of diazomethane, one from N,N'-dinitrosodimethyl oxamide[22] and the other from the stable potassium salt of N-nitrosomethylamine,[23a] look promising:

$$CH_3—\underset{\underset{NO}{|}}{N}—\overset{\overset{O}{\|}}{C}—\overset{\overset{O}{\|}}{C}—\underset{\underset{NO}{|}}{N}—CH_3 \xrightarrow{base} 2\ CH_2N_2 \quad (5\text{-}21a)$$

$$CH_3N\overset{..}{H}_2 + NOCl + KOC_2H_5 \rightarrow CH_3—N{=}N—OK \rightarrow CH_2N_2 \quad (5\text{-}21b)$$

The 1,3-dipolar addition[23b] of nitrous oxide to triphenylphosphine methylene resulted in the formation of **diazomethane** and **triphenylphosphine oxide**:

$$\phi_3\overset{+}{P}-\overset{-}{C}H_2 + N_2O \rightarrow \left[\begin{array}{c} \phi_3P\text{---}CH_2 \\ O \qquad N \\ N \end{array}\right] \rightarrow \phi_3\overset{+}{P}-\overset{-}{O} + CH_2N_2 \quad (5\text{-}21c)$$

The oxidation of hydrazones (method b) is fairly general, but is inconvenient because of the instability of the hydrazones, which must be oxidized as soon as they are prepared. However, for large runs of diazoalkanes other than diazomethane, this method is probably the most practical. The nitrosation of amines is a preparative method subject to the structural limitations previously mentioned.

Despite the apparent differences between the methods for the synthesis of diazoalkanes, one common feature can be recognized; they all involve the elimination of HOR'' from the starting material:

$$\begin{array}{c} R \\ \diagdown \\ C\text{---}N{=}N\text{---}O\text{---}R'' \xrightarrow{-HOR''} \\ \diagup \quad | \\ R' \quad H \end{array} \qquad \begin{array}{c} R \\ \diagdown \\ \overset{}{C}\text{---}N{=}\overset{+}{N} \xleftarrow{-HOR''} \\ \diagup \\ R' \end{array}$$

$$\begin{array}{c} R \qquad\qquad OR'' \\ \diagdown \qquad\qquad \diagup \\ C{=}N\text{---}N \qquad (5\text{-}22) \\ \diagup \qquad\qquad \diagdown \\ R' \qquad\qquad H \end{array}$$

$$\left(R'' = \text{---H, ---HgOH, ---} \overset{\overset{\textstyle O}{\|}}{C}R, \text{ ---SO}_2R, \text{ etc.} \right)$$

This emphasizes again the importance of the elimination of an α-proton and points to the fundamental difference between diazoalkanes and diazonium salts.

Reactions

A detailed discussion of the many and varied reactions of diazoalkanes is beyond the scope of this book. Several good reviews[1b,24] have appeared, and the reader is referred to them for further details on the reactions and uses of these compounds. Only the more recent and the more interesting reactions will be discussed. It will suffice to emphasize the nucleophilic and electrophilic character of diazoalkanes and miscellaneous other features. An understanding of these properties will help explain almost all of their reactions.

Reactions as Nucleophiles. By far the most common reactions of diazoalkanes are those in which they act as nucleophiles, the α-carbon being most often the nucleophilic center. In general, the ease of reaction decreases with decreasing basicity of the α-carbon as exemplified by the wide difference in reactivity between diazomethane and diazoacetic esters (reflected also in their preparation; see "Preparation"). As might be expected, steric effects become important also when the α-carbon is substituted by bulky groups.

With Acids. 1. Mineral acids protonate the α-carbon, and the resulting diazonium ion (XIII) can be attacked by various nucleophiles. β-Elimination of a proton will give an olefin but rearrangements can occur, also. The nature of the solvent is often critical in determining the formation of the products:[25]

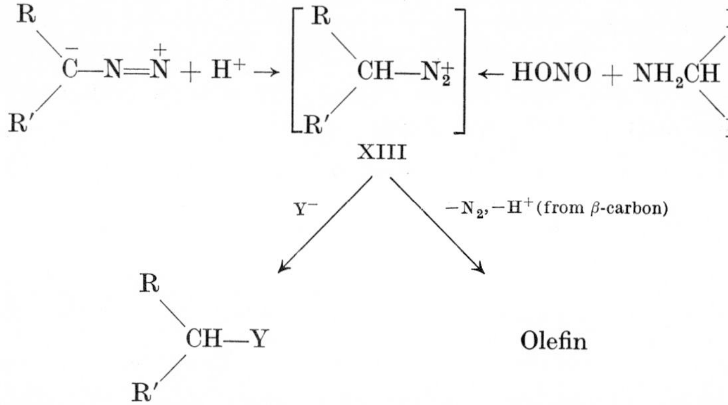

$$
\begin{array}{c}
R \\
\diagdown \\
\overset{-}{C}-N\!\!=\!\!\overset{+}{N} + H^+ \rightarrow \\
\diagup \\
R'
\end{array}
\left[
\begin{array}{c}
R \\
\diagdown \\
CH-N_2^+ \\
\diagup \\
R'
\end{array}
\right]
\leftarrow HONO + NH_2\overset{R}{\underset{R'}{\overset{|}{C}H}}
$$

$$\text{XIII}$$

$$Y^- \swarrow \qquad \searrow -N_2, -H^+ \,(\text{from } \beta\text{-carbon})$$

$$
\begin{array}{c}
R \\
\diagdown \\
CH-Y \\
\diagup \\
R'
\end{array}
\qquad\qquad \text{Olefin} \qquad\qquad (5\text{--}23)
$$

2. The use of diazoalkanes, particularly diazomethane, as alkylating agents offer, the advantages of very mild conditions and high yields. While organic acids react without catalysts, the presence of Lewis acids is necessary for the alkylation of weakly acidic compounds such as alcohols, amines, and enols:

$$R-COOH + CH_2N_2 \rightarrow R-COOCH_3 + N_2 \qquad (5\text{--}24)$$

$$R-OH + CH_2H_2 \xrightarrow{BF_3} R-OCH_3 + N_2 \qquad (5\text{--}25)$$

With Unsaturated Systems. 1. *Carbonyl Compounds.* The following scheme depicts the nucleophilic reaction of diazoalkanes with carbonyl compounds. The intermediate zwitterion can undergo several reactions:

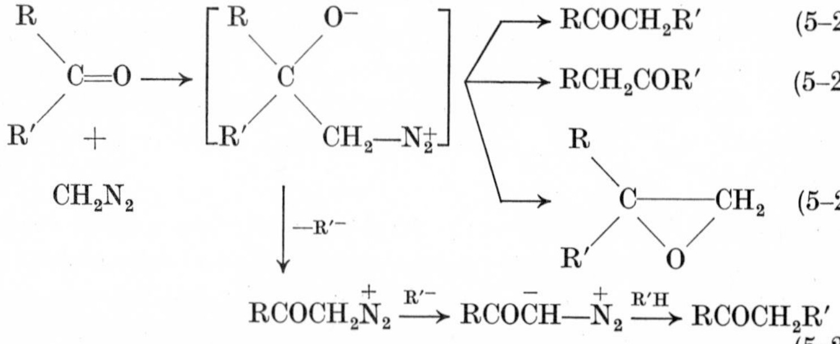

$$
\begin{array}{c}
R \\
\diagdown \\
C\!\!=\!\!O \longrightarrow \\
\diagup \\
R' \quad + \\
\\
CH_2N_2
\end{array}
\left[
\begin{array}{c}
R \qquad O^- \\
\diagdown\;\;\diagup \\
C \\
\diagup\;\;\diagdown \\
R' \qquad CH_2-N_2^+
\end{array}
\right]
\begin{array}{l}
\nearrow RCOCH_2R' \qquad (5\text{--}26a) \\
\\
\leftarrow RCH_2COR' \qquad (5\text{--}26b) \\
\\
\qquad R \\
\qquad \diagdown \\
\searrow \quad C\!\!-\!\!-\!\!-\!\!CH_2 \quad (5\text{--}26c) \\
\qquad \diagup\;\diagdown\;\;\diagup \\
\qquad R' \quad\; O
\end{array}
$$

$$\Big\downarrow {-R'^-}$$

$$RCOCH_2\overset{+}{N}_2 \xrightarrow{R'^-} RCO\overset{-}{C}H-\overset{+}{N}_2 \xrightarrow{R'H} RCOCH_2R'$$

$$(5\text{--}26d)$$

Reactions (5–26a, b, c) occur with aldehydes and ketones. The ring expansion of cyclic ketones[17] is a useful alternative to the Tiffeneau-Demjanov reaction.[26a] With α-diketones or α-oximinoketones, cyclic products are often obtained:

$$
\begin{array}{c}
\text{C}=\text{O} \\
| \\
\text{C}=\text{O}
\end{array}
+ \text{CH}_2\text{N}_2 \rightarrow
\begin{array}{c}
\text{C}=\text{O} \\
\| \\
\text{C}
\end{array}
\text{CH}_2 + \text{N}_2
\qquad (5\text{–}27)
$$

Ketene reacts with diazomethane to give cyclopropanone, which reacts with diazomethane to form cyclobutanone; this is to be contrasted with the reaction of diphenylketene with diphenyldiazomethane, which gives an oxadiazoline.[26b] Steric requirements mentioned previously are important in this case. It is interesting to note that diazomethane reacts with cyclopropenone, not at the carbonyl group but at the $\text{C}=\text{C}$ bonds:[26c]

$$
\text{CH}_2=\text{C}=\text{O} + {}^-\text{CH}_2-\overset{+}{\text{N}}_2 \rightarrow \text{CH}_2=\text{C}-\text{O}^- \longrightarrow
$$

$$
\begin{array}{c}
\text{CH}_2\text{—CH}_2 \\
\diagdown \diagup \\
\text{C} \\
\| \\
\text{O}
\end{array}
\xrightarrow{\text{CH}_2\text{N}_2}
\begin{array}{c}
\text{CH}_2\text{—CH}_2 \\
| \quad | \\
\text{CH}_2\text{—C} \\
\diagdown \\
\text{O}
\end{array}
\qquad (5\text{–}28a)
$$

$$
\begin{array}{c}
\phi \\
\diagdown \\
\text{C}=\text{C}=\text{O} \\
\diagup \\
\phi
\end{array}
+
\begin{array}{c}
\phi \\
\diagdown \\
{}^-\text{C}-\overset{+}{\text{N}}=\text{N} \\
\diagup \\
\phi
\end{array}
\rightarrow
\qquad (5\text{–}28b)
$$

$$
\text{R}\text{—}\!\!\bigtriangleup\!\!\text{—R} + {}^-\text{CH}_2\text{—}\overset{+}{\text{N}}=\text{N} \rightarrow
\left[
\begin{array}{c}
\text{N} \\
\text{CH}_2 \quad \text{N} \\
\text{R}\!\!\bigtriangleup\!\!\text{R} \\
\text{O}
\end{array}
\right]
\rightarrow
\text{R}\text{—}\!\!\text{—R}
$$

$$
\qquad (5\text{–}28c)
$$

Reactions with acid chlorides are represented by reaction (5–26d), R′ being chlorine. The diazoketone will react with the hydrogen halide (R′H) formed to yield an α-haloketone, unless there is a base present to neutralize it. Usually an excess of diazomethane is added, although triethylamine has been used.[27]   Diazoketones can undergo several reactions,[28a] one of which is the Wolff rearrangement, an intermediate step in the Arndt-Eistert synthesis.[29] Esters, amides, and similar compounds, where the positive nature of the carbonyl carbon is diminished, do not react with diazoalkanes. Sulfonyl halides do not react with diazoalkanes. Fahr[28b] recently reported the formation of "inner salts" with Lewis acids.

2. *Nitriles, Azomethines, Nitroso and Azo Compounds.*   Typical examples of the reactions of diazomethane with nitriles, azomethines and nitroso compounds are given below:

$$R\!-\!C\!\!\equiv\!\!N + CH_2N_2 \rightarrow R\!-\!\overset{\displaystyle |}{\underset{\displaystyle CH_2}{C}}\!\!=\!\!=\!\!\overset{\displaystyle |}{\underset{\displaystyle N}{N}} \longrightarrow$$

$$R\!-\!\overset{\displaystyle |}{\underset{\displaystyle CH}{C}}\!\!=\!\!=\!\!\overset{\displaystyle |}{\underset{\displaystyle NH}{N}} \;\;\xrightarrow{CH_2N_2}\;\; R\!-\!\overset{\displaystyle |}{\underset{\displaystyle CH}{C}}\!\!=\!\!=\!\!\overset{\displaystyle |}{\underset{\displaystyle N-CH_3}{N}} \qquad (5\text{-}29)$$

$$R\!-\!CH\!\!=\!\!N\!-\!R' + CH_2N_2 \rightarrow R\!-\!\overset{\displaystyle |}{\underset{\displaystyle CH_2}{CH}}\!\!-\!\!-\!\!\overset{\displaystyle |}{\underset{\displaystyle N}{N}}\!-\!R' \qquad (5\text{-}30)^{28c}$$

$$R\!-\!N\!\!=\!\!O + CH_2N_2 \rightarrow \left[R\!-\!N \overset{O}{\underset{}{\diagup\!\diagdown}} CH_2 \right] \rightarrow R\!-\!\overset{O^-}{\underset{+}{N}}\!\!=\!\!CH_2 \qquad (5\text{-}31)$$

Some interesting abnormal reactions have been reported. Diazomethane does not add across the —C≡N in compound XIV. Rather, N-methylation occurs:[30]

$$\begin{array}{c} CH_3SO_2 \\ \diagdown \\ CH_3SO_2 \diagup \end{array}\!\!CH\!-\!C\!\!\equiv\!\!N \longrightarrow \begin{array}{c} CH_3SO_2 \\ \diagdown \\ CH_3SO_2 \diagup \end{array}\!\!C\!\!=\!\!C\!\!=\!\!NH \;\xrightarrow{CH_2N_2}$$

XIV

$$\begin{array}{c} CH_3SO_2 \\ \diagdown \\ CH_3SO_2 \diagup \end{array}\!\!C\!\!=\!\!C\!\!=\!\!N\!-\!CH_3 \qquad (5\text{-}32)$$

With the oxime ether XV, addition across the $\diagdown$C$=$N$-$ bond takes place :[31]

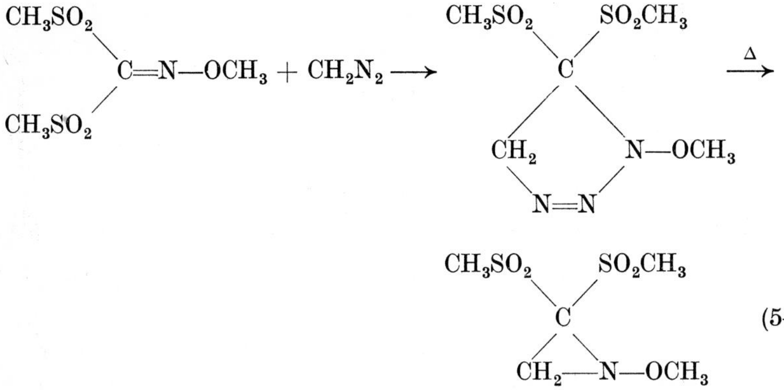

$$\begin{array}{c} CH_3SO_2 \\ \diagdown \\ \diagup \\ CH_3SO_2 \end{array} C=N-OCH_3 + CH_2N_2 \longrightarrow$$

(5-33)

The important studies of Leonard and co-workers on the reaction of diazomethane with iminium salts $\left[\diagdown C=\overset{+}{N} \diagup \right]$ have culminated in the recent report[32] of the ring expansion of cyclic iminium salts:

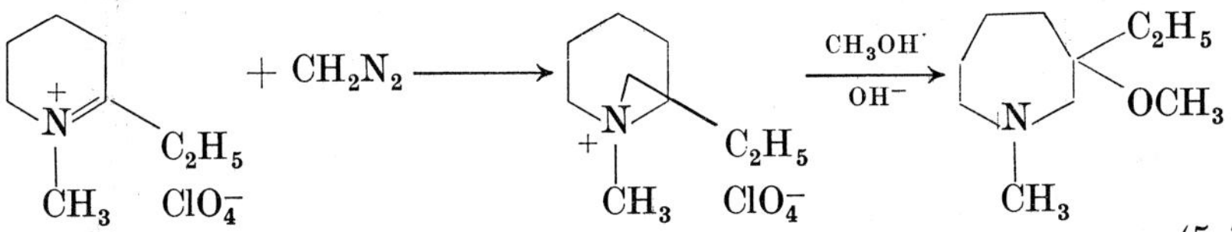

(5-34)

Although it has been shown[33a] that the reaction of diazoalkanes with azodicarbonyl compounds does not give the diazacyclopropanes, but rather oxadiazolines, Russian workers have recently claimed[34] that hexafluoroazomethane reacts with diazomethane to yield two addition products:

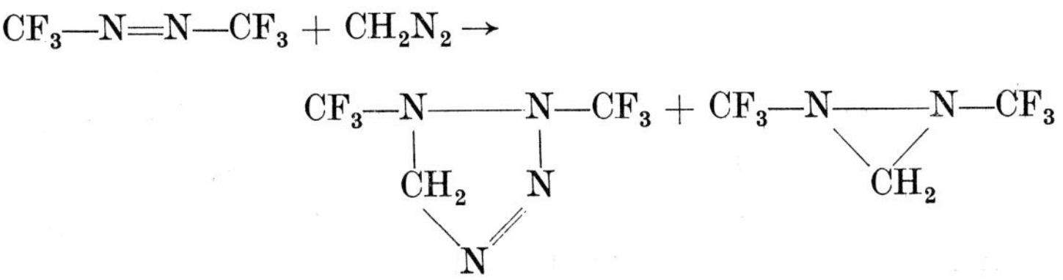

$$CF_3-N=N-CF_3 + CH_2N_2 \rightarrow$$

(5-35)

The reaction of diazoketones with azodicarboxylic esters involves several rearrangements.[33b]   The simplified reaction is given in (5–36):

$$R-\overset{\overset{O}{\|}}{C}-\overset{-}{C}H-\overset{+}{N}{\equiv}N + C_2H_5OOCN{=}NCOOC_2H_5 \rightarrow$$

$$R-\overset{\overset{O}{\|}}{C}-CH{=}N-N\overset{\displaystyle COOC_2H_5}{\underset{\displaystyle COOC_2H_5}{\big<}} \qquad (5\text{–}36)$$

3. *Other Hetero-unsaturated Systems.* Diazoalkanes react with diaryl-carbodiimides, isocyanates, isothiocyanates, and thiocarbonyl compounds:

$$\phi N{=}C{=}O \nearrow \left[\begin{matrix}\phi-N\!-\!\!-\!\!-C{=}O\\ \diagdown\;\;CH_2\;\;\diagup\end{matrix}\right] \xrightarrow{\;CH_2N_2\;} \begin{matrix}\phi-N\!-\!\!-\!\!-C{=}O\\ |\qquad\quad|\\ CH_2-CH_2\end{matrix} \qquad (5\text{–}37a)$$

$$CH_2N_2 \xrightarrow{\;\phi N{=}C{=}S\;} \phi-NH-C\overset{\overset{\displaystyle S}{\diagup\diagdown}}{\underset{\underset{\displaystyle CH-\!\!-\!\!-N}{\|\quad\;\;\|}}{\quad N}} \qquad (5\text{–}37b)$$

$$\phi CO-N{=}C{=}O \searrow \left[\begin{matrix}\overset{\displaystyle N}{\diagup\;\diagdown}\\ \phi-C\qquad C{=}O\\ |\qquad\quad|\\ O\!\!\diagup\!\!\diagdown CH_2-\overset{+}{N_2}\end{matrix}\right] \longrightarrow \phi-C\overset{\overset{\displaystyle N}{\diagup\;\diagdown}}{\underset{\underset{\displaystyle O\!-\!\!-\!\!-CH_2}{|\qquad\quad|}}{\qquad C{=}O}} \qquad (5\text{–}37c)$$

4. *Carbon-Carbon Unsaturated Systems.* The addition of diazoalkanes to unsaturated C—C bonds has been known for a long time.   In most instances, the primary addition product (i.e., without loss of nitrogen) or an isomer thereof may be isolated.   In many cases involving hetero-unsaturated systems, such adducts are also formed.   This type of addition constitutes a part of the extremely important 1,3-dipolar addition reactions[13a] (5–38). This subject has been reviewed by Huisgen,[35] who defined and broadened the scope of this very versatile reaction:

$$\begin{matrix}R\\ \diagdown\\ \;\;\;\overset{-}{C}-\overset{+}{N}{=}N \rightarrow\\ \diagup\\ R'\end{matrix} \qquad \begin{matrix}R\qquad N{=}N\\ \diagdown\quad\diagup\qquad\diagdown\\ \;\;C\qquad\qquad b\\ \diagup\quad\diagdown\qquad\diagup\\ R'\qquad\qquad a\end{matrix} \qquad (5\text{–}38)$$

$$\overset{+}{a{=}b}$$

In general, an activated unsaturated carbon-carbon bond will react with diazoalkanes to give a heterocyclic compound.   The ease and the direction of addition are affected by both electronic and steric factors.   Alkynes yield pyrazoles (5–39a), and olefins yield 1-pyrazolines (XVI), which usually isomerize to the 2-isomers (XVII) when α-hydrogens are available and when this results in the formation of a conjugated system (5–39b):

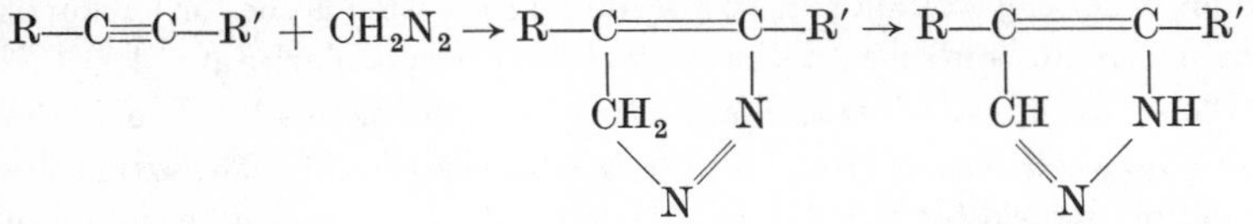

$$R-C\equiv C-R' + CH_2N_2 \rightarrow R-C=C-R' \rightarrow R-C=C-R' \quad (5\text{–}39a)$$

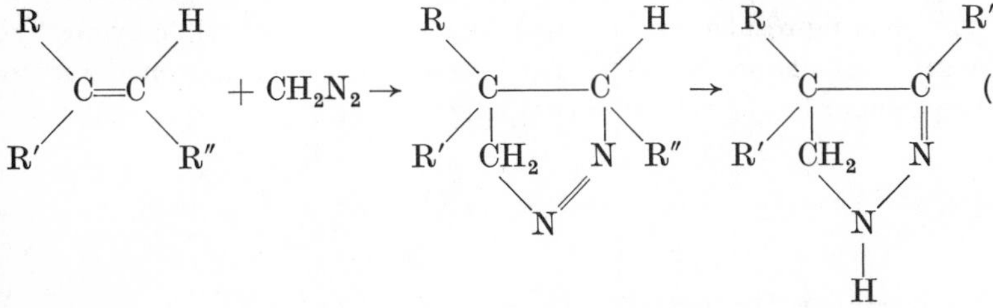

$$(5\text{–}39b)$$

XVI   XVII

However, there are cases of stable 1-pyrazolines even when the driving force for isomerization is very strong.[36] The addition of diazoalkanes to olefins has been claimed to involve a concerted addition[35] and has been viewed as a *cis*-addition.[37] Recent evidence,[38] involving stereospecific addition of diazomethane to the isomeric, unsaturated esters methyl angelate and methyl tiglate, to produce single, isomeric products in each case, would seem to support the postulated mechanism. However, this mechanism cannot be applied to all 1,3-dipolar additions of diazoalkanes, since the reaction of *p*-methoxy styrene to *p*-(methoxyphenyl)diazomethane gave a mixture of the corresponding *cis*- and *trans*-1-pyrazolines:[20,38b]

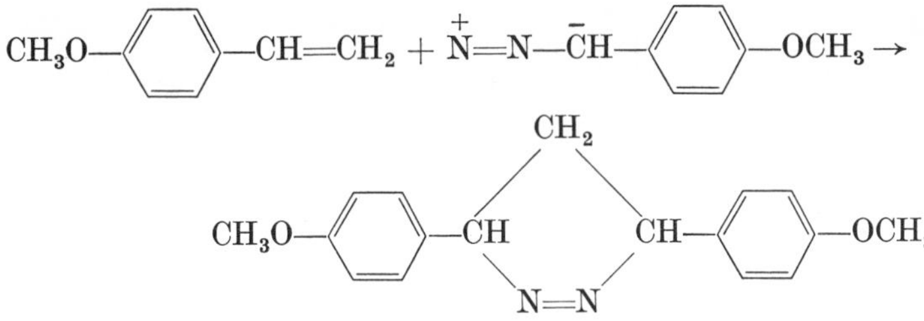

$$(5\text{–}40a)$$

The first examples of the methylation of a vinyl hydrogen in three steps via diazomethane addition to a benzalmalononitrile have been reported:[39]

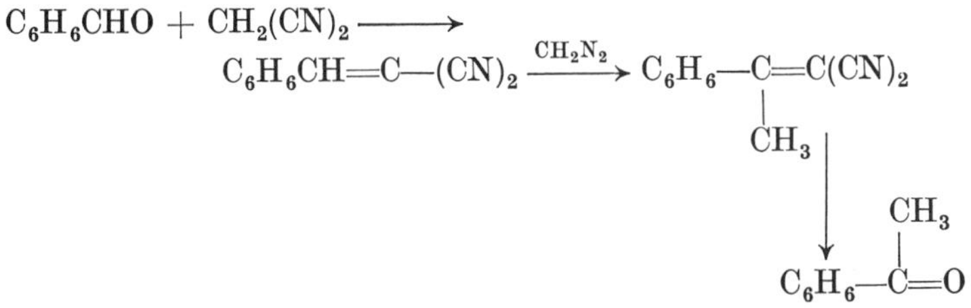

$$C_6H_6CHO + CH_2(CN)_2 \longrightarrow$$
$$C_6H_6CH=C-(CN)_2 \xrightarrow{CH_2N_2} C_6H_6-C=C(CN)_2$$

$$(5\text{–}40b)$$

Other Nucleophilic Reactions. Diazoalkanes react at the carbon atom with various other electrophiles.[24]   Expecially interesting is the formation of chlorodiazomethane from diazomethane and *t*-butyl hypochlorite at $-100°C$.[40] Dihalocarbenes react with diazoalkanes to give halo olefins.[41]   The boron trifluoride–catalyzed polymerization of diazoalkanes provides two examples of electrophilic attack by the catalyst (BF_3) and the incipient carbonium ion.[42a]   Interesting results are obtained by the reaction of triphenylmethyl cation with diazoalkanes.[42b]   The ozonolysis of diphenyldiazomethane to give benzophenone has been pictured as going through the following scheme:[43]

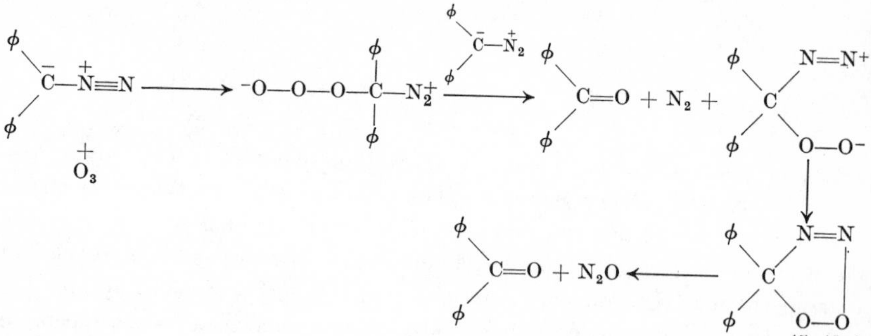

(5–41a)

The attack of sulfur dioxide on diazoalkanes presumably involves "sulfenes" as intermediates:[44]

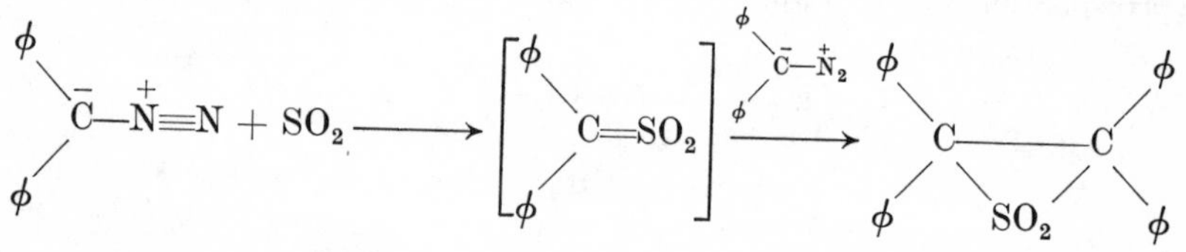

(5–41b)

Other examples of electrophilic attack include the reaction of zinc iodide[45] and of *p*-nitrobenzenediazonium chloride. In these cases, the products resulting from electrophilic reaction at the terminal nitrogen are, along with the formation of azine from the decomposition of diazoalkanes,[74] among the few examples of reaction at this site. Bis-(trifluoromethyl)diazomethane reacts with cyclohexane, probably via a radical process, to give an azo compound:[76]

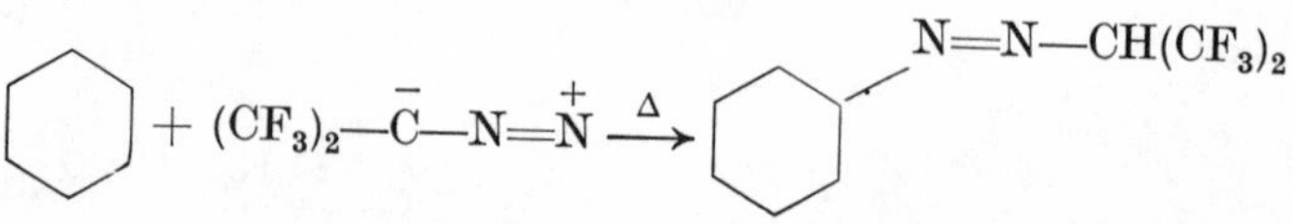

(5–41c)

Reactions as Electrophiles. The behavior of diazoalkanes as electrophiles is much less pronounced, and the examples are few. Diazoacetophenone reacts with cyanide to give the cyanohydrazone of phenylglyoxal. Phosphazines result from the reaction of diazoalkanes with tertiary phosphines:

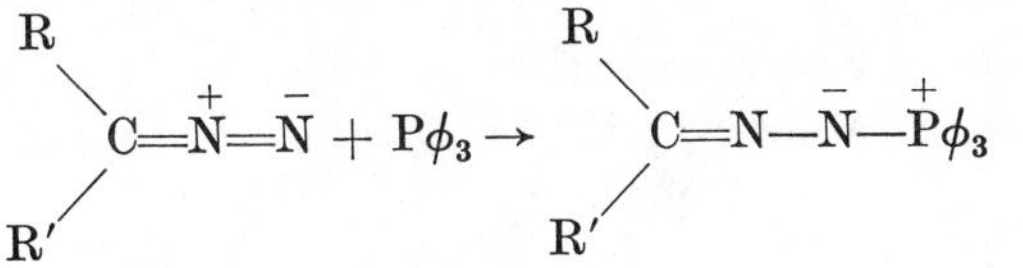

$$\begin{array}{c} R \\ \diagdown \\ C{=}\overset{+}{N}{=}\overset{-}{N} + P\phi_3 \rightarrow \\ \diagup \\ R' \end{array} \qquad \begin{array}{c} R \\ \diagdown \\ C{=}N{-}\overset{-}{N}{-}\overset{+}{P}\phi_3 \\ \diagup \\ R' \end{array} \qquad (5\text{-}42)$$

In the presence of copper, ylids are obtained, while azine also can be formed.[46a] The reaction of diphenyldiazomethane with tri-isopropylphosphite[46b] is of interest:

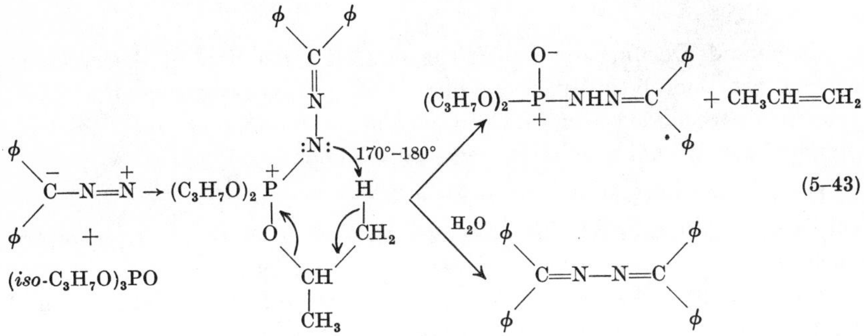

$$(5\text{-}43)$$

Amines and hydrazines[47a] also can attack diazoalkanes. It has been reported[47b] that diazodimedone undergoes "coupling" with activated aromatic compounds. The reaction of diazoketones with active methylene usually leads to the formation of pyrazoles. Farnum and Yates[48] have reported a diazo transfer reaction:

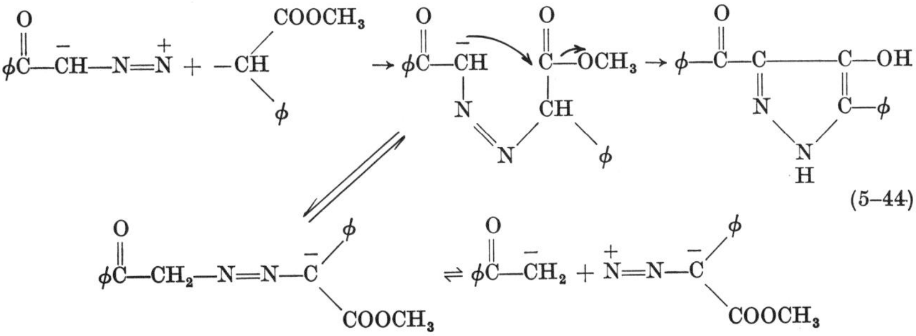

$$(5\text{-}44)$$

Grignard reagents attack diazoalkanes to form substituted hydrazones:

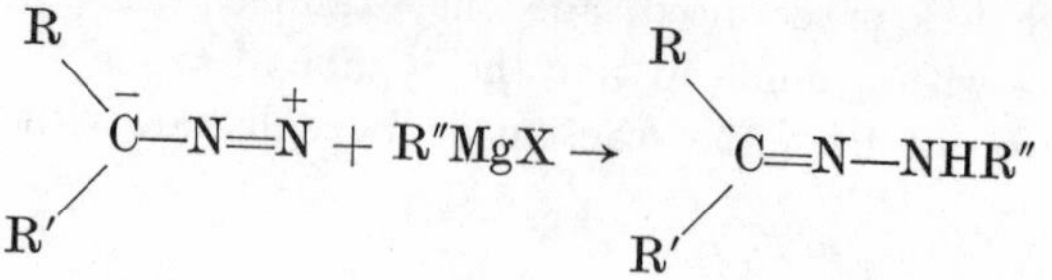

$$\begin{array}{c} R \\ \diagdown \\ \overset{-}{C}-N{=}\overset{+}{N} \\ \diagup \\ R' \end{array} + R''MgX \rightarrow \begin{array}{c} R \\ \diagdown \\ C{=}N-NHR'' \\ \diagup \\ R' \end{array} \qquad (5\text{-}45)$$

Strong bases such as methyllithium convert diazomethane to the diazomethyl anion which, upon acid hydrolysis, gives isodiazomethane (XVIII):[49]

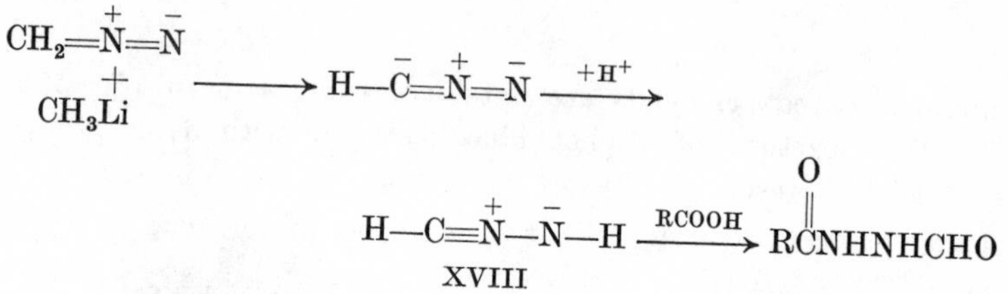

$$\begin{array}{c} CH_2{=}\overset{+}{N}{=}\overset{-}{N} \\ + \\ CH_3Li \end{array} \longrightarrow H-\overset{-}{C}{=}\overset{+}{N}{=}\overset{-}{N} \xrightarrow{+H^+}$$

$$H-C{\equiv}\overset{+}{N}-\overset{-}{N}-H \xrightarrow{RCOOH} R\overset{\overset{O}{\|}}{C}NHNHCHO \qquad (5\text{-}46)$$

XVIII

Carbenoid Decomposition. In general, the reaction of diazoalkanes carried out photolytically or thermally with catalysts yields the corresponding carbenes, which undergo several reactions that have been reviewed[50] and are not within the scope of this book.

Miscellaneous Reactions. The reactions of diazoalkanes with free radicals are few. Hexaphenylpropane was isolated from the reaction of triphenylmethyl radical with diazomethane.[51] Reaction of diazoalkanes with nickel tetracarbonyl may or may not involve free radicals.[52] The action of nitric oxide leads to a series of very interesting reactions:[53a]

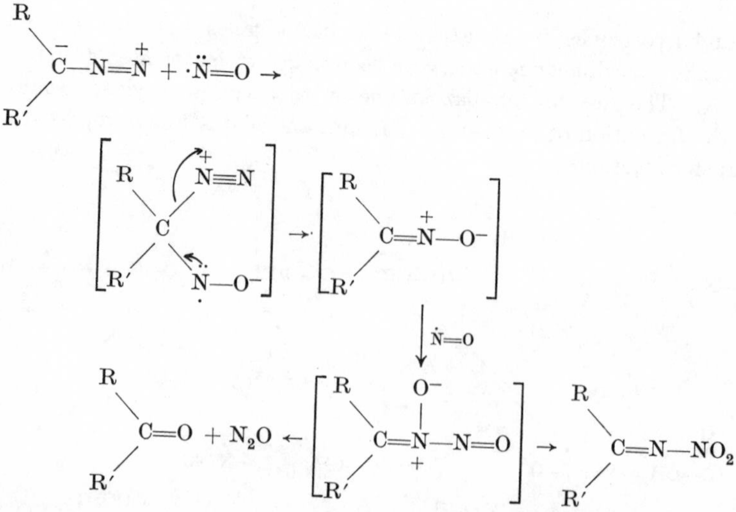

$$\begin{array}{c} R \\ \diagdown \\ \overset{-}{C}-N{=}\overset{+}{N} \\ \diagup \\ R' \end{array} + \cdot\ddot{N}{=}O \rightarrow$$

$$\left[\begin{array}{c} R \quad \overset{+}{N}{\equiv}N \\ \diagdown \diagup \\ C \\ \diagup \diagdown \\ R' \quad \overset{\cdot\cdot}{N}-O^- \end{array}\right] \rightarrow \cdot\left[\begin{array}{c} R \\ \diagdown \\ C{=}\overset{+}{N}-O^- \\ \diagup \\ R' \end{array}\right]$$

$$\downarrow \dot{N}{=}O \qquad\qquad (5\text{-}47a)$$

$$\begin{array}{c} R \\ \diagdown \\ C{=}O \\ \diagup \\ R' \end{array} + N_2O \leftarrow \left[\begin{array}{c} R \quad O^- \\ \diagdown \quad | \\ C{=}N-N{=}O \\ \diagup \quad + \\ R' \end{array}\right] \rightarrow \begin{array}{c} R \\ \diagdown \\ C{=}N-NO_2 \\ \diagup \\ R' \end{array}$$

Other reactions have been reported.[53b] Somewhat similar is the action of sodium metal on diazofluorene:[54]

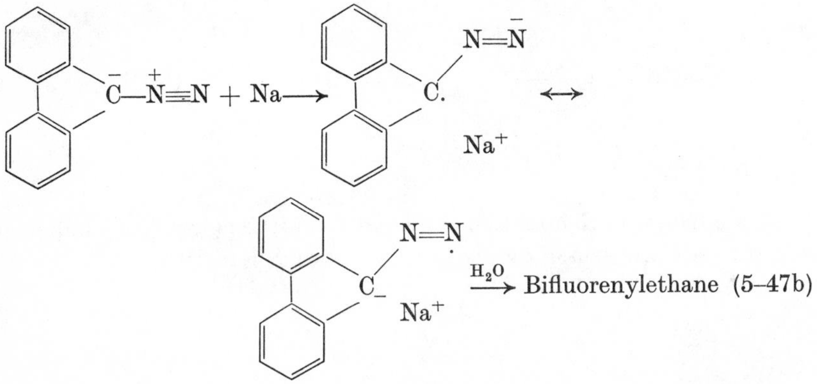

Bifluorenylethane (5–47b)

The reduction of diazoalkanes gives various products, depending upon the method of reduction and the nature of the substituents:[53c]

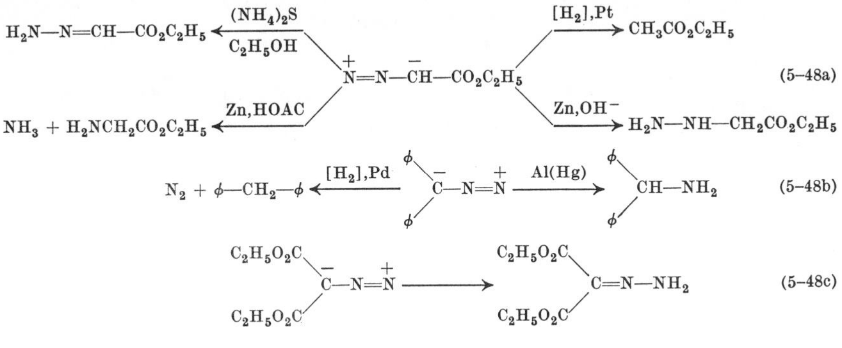

$$H_2N-N=CH-CO_2C_2H_5 \xleftarrow[C_2H_5OH]{(NH_4)_2S}$$

$$\xrightarrow[]{[H_2],Pt} CH_3CO_2C_2H_5$$

$$\overset{+}{N}=N-\overset{-}{C}H-CO_2C_2H_5 \qquad (5\text{–}48a)$$

$$NH_3 + H_2NCH_2CO_2C_2H_5 \xleftarrow{Zn,HOAC}$$

$$\xrightarrow{Zn,OH^-} H_2N-NH-CH_2CO_2C_2H_5$$

$$N_2 + \phi-CH_2-\phi \xleftarrow{[H_2],Pd} \underset{\phi}{\overset{\phi}{\diagup}}\overset{-}{C}-N=\overset{+}{N} \xrightarrow{Al(Hg)} \underset{\phi}{\overset{\phi}{\diagup}}CH-NH_2 \qquad (5\text{–}48b)$$

$$\underset{C_2H_5O_2C}{\overset{C_2H_5O_2C}{\diagup}}\overset{-}{C}-N=\overset{+}{N} \longrightarrow \underset{C_2H_5O_2C}{\overset{C_2H_5O_2C}{\diagup}}C=N-NH_2 \qquad (5\text{–}48c)$$

Diazoalkanes as Intermediates and Products

This section describes some interesting reactions in which the formation of diazoalkanes as intermediates or products is indicated. In many cases, they have been isolated and characterized; in other instances, indirect evidence strongly suggests their participation during the reaction.

It has been shown[55] that the free radical oxidation of hydrazones to azines does not involve the intermediacy of diazoalkanes. Recently, this difference in mechanism has been clearly demonstrated;[56] the oxidation of benzo-phenone hydrazone with iodine gave the azine, while, when triethylamine was present, diphenyldiazomethane could be isolated:

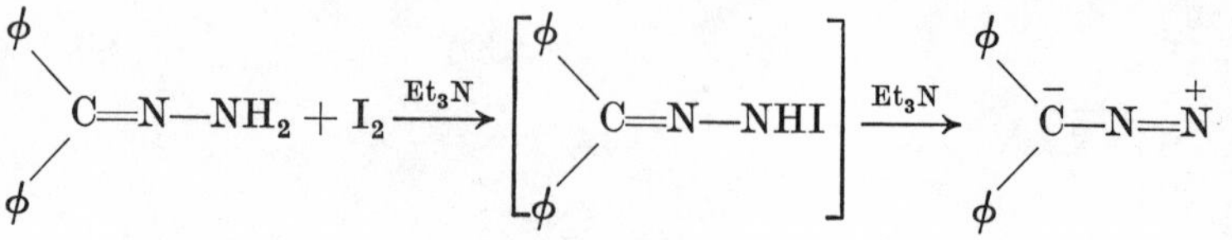

$$\begin{matrix}\phi \\ \\ \phi\end{matrix}\text{C=N—NH}_2 + \text{I}_2 \xrightarrow{\text{Et}_3\text{N}} \left[\begin{matrix}\phi \\ \\ \phi\end{matrix}\text{C=N—NHI}\right] \xrightarrow{\text{Et}_3\text{N}} \begin{matrix}\phi \\ \\ \phi\end{matrix}\overset{-}{\text{C}}\text{—N}\overset{+}{\text{=N}} \quad (5\text{-}49)$$

The products of the reaction of hydrazones with halogenated 1,2-quinones suggest the formation of diazoalkanes as intermediates:[57]

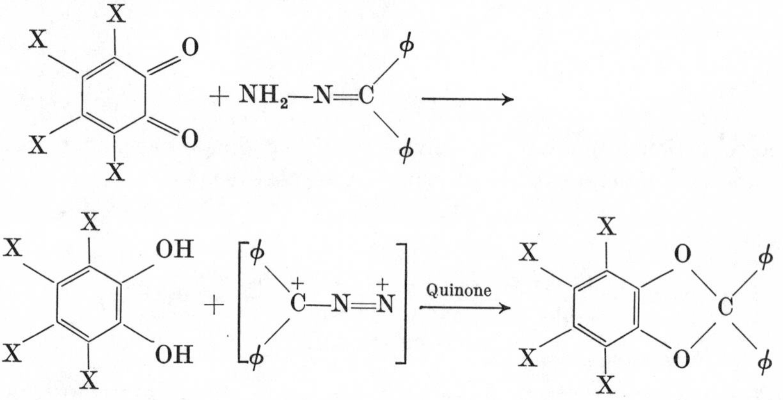

$$(5\text{-}50)$$

Zimmerman and Somasekhara[58] have shown that the pyrolysis of azines to the corresponding olefins involves the diazoalkanes as the chain carrying species:

$$\text{ArCH=N—N=CHAr} + \text{Ar}\overset{-}{\text{CH}}\text{—}\overset{+}{\text{N}}_2 \rightarrow \text{ArCH—}\overset{-}{\text{N}}\text{—N=CHAr}$$

$$\text{Ar}\overset{|}{\text{CH}}\text{—}\overset{+}{\text{N}}_2^+$$

$$\rightarrow \text{Ar}\overset{-}{\text{CH}}\text{—}\overset{+}{\text{N}}_2 + \text{ArCH=CHAr} + \text{N}_2 \quad (5\text{-}51)$$

Bridson-Jones and co-workers[59] have found that the nitrous oxide oxidation of olefins and acetylenes at high temperatures and pressures gave products that could be explained only via the transient formation of diazoalkanes (5–52a):

$$
\begin{array}{c}
\underset{R_2}{\overset{R_1}{>}}C{=}C\underset{R_4}{\overset{R_3}{<}} \\
+ \\
N_2O
\end{array}
\rightarrow
\begin{array}{c}
\underset{R_2}{\overset{R_1}{>}}C{-}C\underset{N}{\overset{R_3}{<}}R_4 \\
O \\
\end{array}
\rightarrow
\underset{R_2}{\overset{R_1}{>}}C{=}O +
\underset{R_4}{\overset{R_3}{>}}C{-}\overset{+}{N}{=}\overset{-}{N}
\qquad (5\text{-}52a)
$$

$$
\begin{array}{c}
\underset{R_2}{\overset{R_1}{>}}C{-}C\underset{N}{\overset{R_3}{<}}R_4 \\
O^- \quad \overset{+}{N}
\end{array}
\xrightarrow{-N_2}
\underset{R_2}{\overset{R_1}{>}}C{-}C\underset{R_4}{\overset{R_3}{<}} \quad \rightarrow \text{products} \qquad (5\text{-}52b) \\
O^-
$$

The distribution of products is highly dependent upon the nature of the olefins. It is also to be noted that the primary adduct is the same as that obtained from the addition of diazoalkanes to aldehydes and ketones. Diazoalkanes were shown[60] to be products of the decomposition of azine monoxides (XIX) (5–53) and of the oxidation of hydrazones with peracetic acid:

$$
\underset{R}{\overset{Ar}{>}}C{=}\overset{+}{N}{-}N{=}C\underset{R}{\overset{Ar}{<}}
\rightarrow
\left[\underset{R}{\overset{Ar}{>}}C{-}N{-}N{=}C\underset{R}{\overset{Ar}{<}} \right]
\rightarrow
$$

$$
\qquad\qquad\qquad O_- \qquad\qquad\qquad\qquad O
$$

$$
\text{XIX}
$$

$$
\underset{R}{\overset{Ar}{>}}C{=}O +
\underset{R}{\overset{Ar}{>}}C{=}\overset{+}{N}{=}\overset{-}{N}
\qquad (5\text{-}53)
$$

The tautomerization of diphenyldiazirine (XX) to diphenyldiazomethane has been recently reported:[61]

$$
\underset{\phi}{\overset{\phi}{>}}C{=}NH + H_2NOSO_3H
\xrightarrow[-70°]{NH_3}
\left[\underset{\phi}{\overset{\phi}{>}}C\underset{NH}{\overset{NH}{<}} \right]
\xrightarrow{[O]}
$$

$$
\left[\underset{\phi}{\overset{\phi}{>}}C\underset{N}{\overset{N}{<}} \right]
\longrightarrow
\underset{\phi}{\overset{\phi}{>}}C{-}\overset{-}{N}{=}\overset{+}{N}
\qquad (5\text{-}54)
$$

$$
\text{XX}
$$

Wibaut and Boon[62] have postulated the formation of dimethyldiazomethane as an intermediate during the ozonolysis of acetone azine:

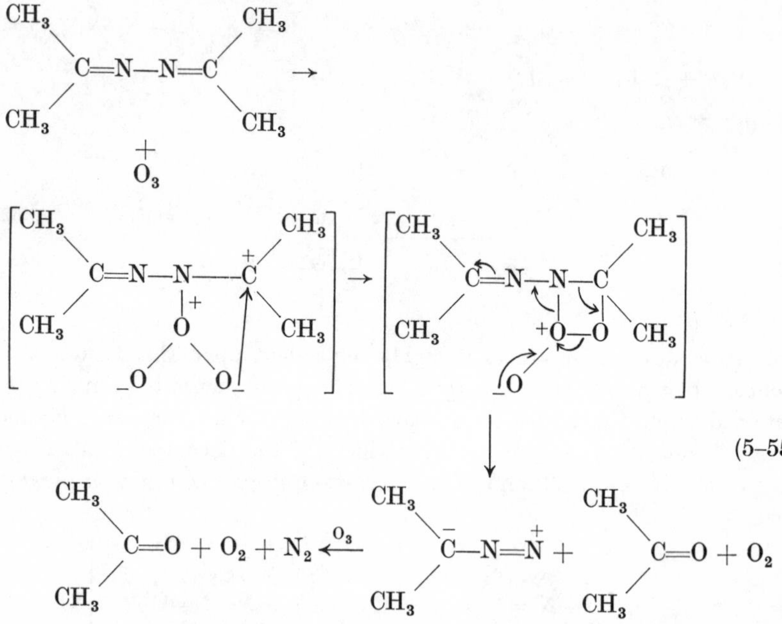

$$(5\text{--}55)$$

The rearrangement of azotriazoles (XXI) to tetrazoles has been viewed by Pedersen[63] as involving a diazoalkane as an intermediate:

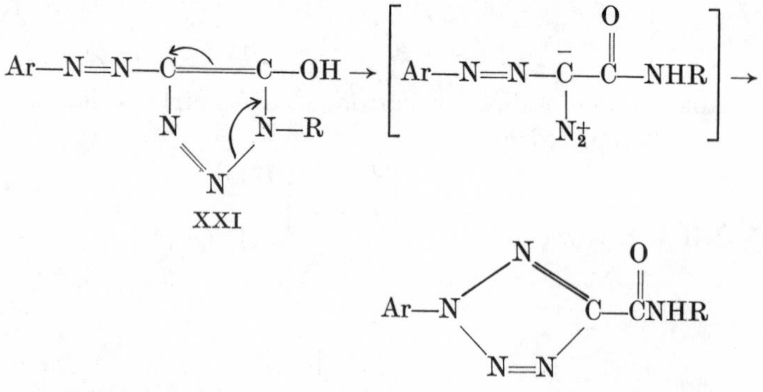

$$(5\text{--}56)$$

Indirect evidence for the formation of diazoalkanes has been obtained in the reaction of nitrous acid with α-aminoketones:[64]

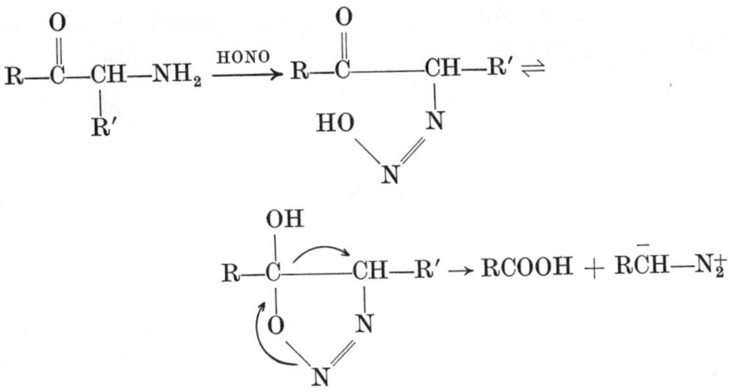

$$R-\overset{\overset{O}{\|}}{C}-\underset{\underset{R'}{|}}{CH}-NH_2 \xrightarrow{\text{HONO}} R-\overset{\overset{O}{\|}}{C}-\underset{\underset{HO}{|}}{CH}-R' \rightleftharpoons$$

$$R-\overset{\overset{OH}{|}}{C}-CH-R' \rightarrow RCOOH + R\bar{C}H-N_2^+ \quad (5\text{-}57)$$

Daeniker and Druey[65] recently reported the formation of N-acetyl diazo-acetamide from the catalytic reduction of the sydnone imine XXII:

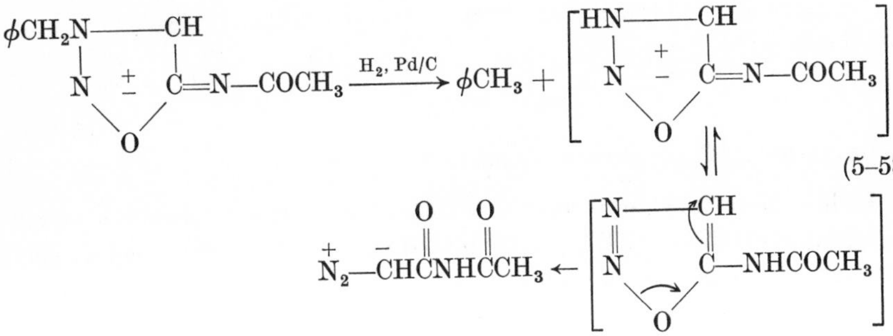

$$\phi CH_2 N - CH \atop N \overset{+}{\underset{-}{}} C = N - COCH_3 \xrightarrow{H_2, \, Pd/C} \phi CH_3 + \left[HN - CH \atop N \overset{+}{-} C = N - COCH_3 \right]$$

$$(5\text{-}58)$$

$$\overset{+}{N_2}-\overset{\overset{O}{\|}}{CHC}\overset{\overset{O}{\|}}{NHCCH_3} \leftarrow \left[N - CH \atop N \quad C - NHCOCH_3 \right]$$

Hindered N-nitrosimines have been reduced to the corresponding diazo-alkanes by lithium aluminum hydride (see Chapter 7).

An unsaturated diazoalkane may be involved during the decomposition of the sodium salt of the tosylhydrazones of α,β-unsaturated ketones:[66]

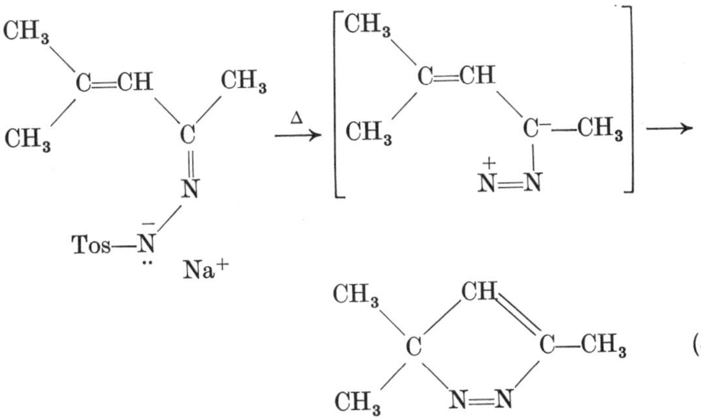

$$\underset{CH_3}{\overset{CH_3}{}}C = CH \quad \underset{C}{\overset{CH_3}{}} \xrightarrow{\Delta} \left[\underset{CH_3}{\overset{CH_3}{}}C = CH \quad \underset{\overset{+}{N}=N}{\overset{C^- - CH_3}{}} \right] \rightarrow$$

$$\text{Tos}-\overset{..}{N} \quad Na^+$$

$$\underset{CH_3}{\overset{CH_3}{}}C \quad \underset{N=N}{\overset{CH}{}}C-CH_3 \quad (5\text{-}59)$$

The loss of diazolkanes from certain compounds formed via 1,3-dipolar addition has been reported:[67]

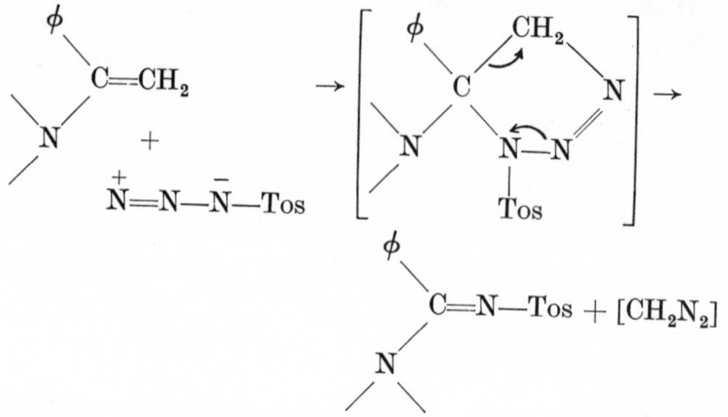

$$C=N-Tos + [CH_2N_2] \quad (5\text{--}60a)$$

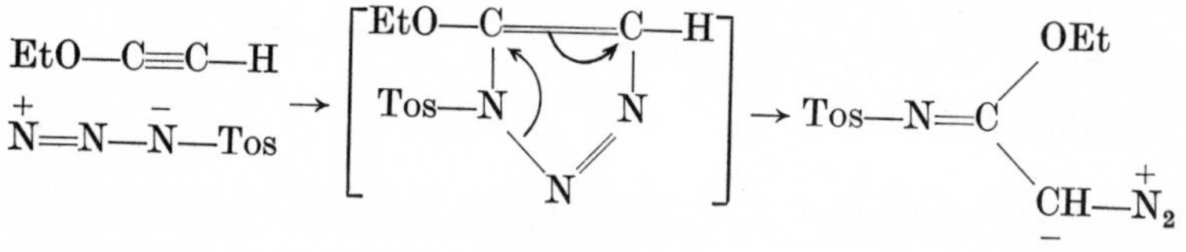

$$(5\text{--}60b)$$

Tautomerism of Diazoalkanes-Diazirines

It has been previously mentioned (see "Structure") that the recent synthesis of diazirines (XII) has eliminated the possibility that such a cyclic structure could be contributing, even to a small degree, to the resonance hybrid of diazoalkanes (XI):

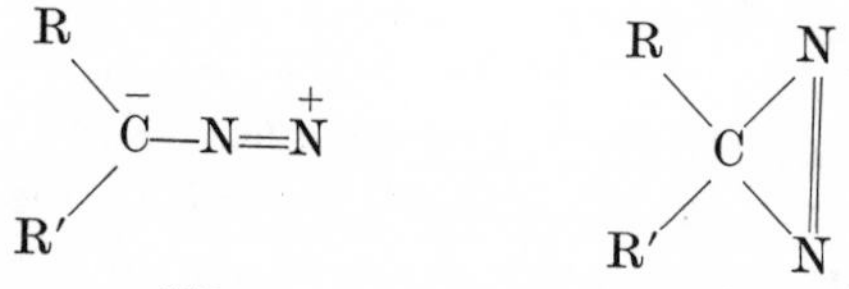

However, this special case of valence tautomerism involves only electrons; XI could be regarded as a diazirine if it is assumed that an "ionic" bond exists between the positive and negative ends of the molecule. A priori, diazoalkanes and diazirines should be interconvertible since the chemistry of nitrones affords a precedent of such a behavior. Indeed, Splitter and Calvin[68a] were able to convert nitrones (XXII) to oxaziranes (XXIV) under the influence of ultraviolet light:

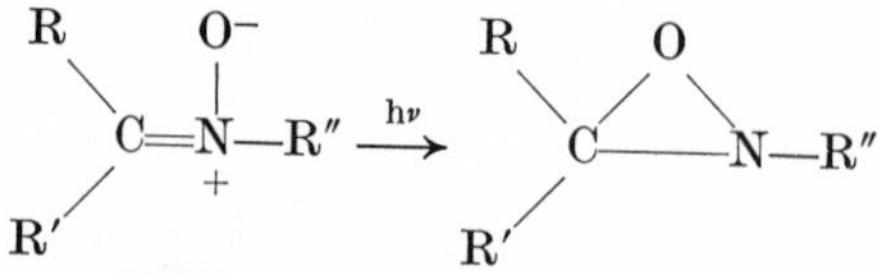

Subsequently, Bonner, Clark, and Todd reported a similar tautomerization.[68b] The thermal conversion of oxaziranes to nitrones is known. Several other reactions of compounds having the $\overset{\displaystyle O^-}{\underset{\diagup}{\overset{\diagdown}{C}}=N^+}$— structure can be explained only via *prior tautomerization* to the cyclic structure.[53,60,69]

The isolation of diphenyldiazomethane[61] from the reaction of benzophenone imine and hydroxylamine-O-sulfonic acid has been ascribed to such a *ring opening* of the corresponding diazirine (see 5–55). A similar behavior was noted when fluorenone imine was reacted with difluoroamine;[70a] diazofluorene was the only product isolated.[70a]

The ultraviolet irradiation of diazirine (XII, R = R' = H) gave diazomethane.[71] Tagging experiments (5–62) provided evidence for the intermediacy of diazirine although disproportionation followed by recombination cannot be ruled out (5–63):[71a]

$$CH_2 \overset{N}{\underset{N}{\diagup\diagdown}} \|\quad \xrightarrow{h\nu,\ Ar}\quad {}^-CH_2 - N = \overset{+}{N} \qquad (5\text{–}61)$$

$$^-CH_2 - {}^{15}N = \overset{+}{N} \xrightarrow{h\nu, Ar} {}^-CH_2 - N = \overset{+}{N}{}^{15} \qquad (5\text{–}62)$$

$$^-CH_2 - {}^{15}N = \overset{+}{N} \xrightarrow{h\nu, N_2} {}^-CH_2 - N = \overset{+}{N} + N \equiv N^{15} \qquad (5\text{–}63)$$

The diazirines are probably at a higher energy level and, as suggested by Splitter and Calvin for the nitrone-oxazirane conversion, the isomerization of diazoalkanes to diazirines constitutes a storage of electromagnetic energy in the form of chemical energy. The term *electroisomerization* (and *electroisomers*) seems to fit best these special cases of valence tautomerism.[72]

Properties of Diazirines.[73] Schmitz and co-workers have done most of the studies on diazirines, which can be prepared by oxidation of the appropriate hydrazines. In contrast to the corresponding diazoalkanes, diazirines are colorless compounds and are much less prone to thermal decomposition which gives the olefin as the sole product. This behavior is to be contrasted with that of the diazoalkanes, which often yield the corresponding azine.[74] The chemical inertness of diazirines may explain the lack of azine formation. Diazirines are fairly stable to strong acids and strong bases. However, they can be reduced to the corresponding hydrazines or to give cleavage products. Reaction with Grignard reagents confirms their cyclic structure (compare with 5–46):

$$(5\text{–}64)$$

Ultraviolet and infrared absorptions correspond to that of *cis* azo compounds (Chapter 4) with no absorption occurring in the visible region. Explosions take place when diazirines are heated strongly. Frey and Stevens[75] have carried out some studies of their photolytic decomposition.

REFERENCES

General

K. SAUNDERS, *The Aromatic Diazo Compounds*, Longmans, Green and Co., London, 1949.

H. ZOLLINGER, *Diazo and Azo Compounds: Aliphatic and Aromatic Compounds*, Interscience Publishers, Inc., New York, 1961.

R. HUISGEN, Aliphatic diazo compounds, *Angew. Chem.*, **67**, 439 (1955).

E. SCHMITZ, in A. R. KATRITZKY, *Advances in Heterocyclic Chemistry*, vol. 2, Academic Press, New York, 1964 p. 83.

Text

1. (a) K. SAUNDERS, *The Aromatic Diazo Compounds*, Longmans, Green and Co., London, 1949.
   (b) H. ZOLLINGER, Diazo and Azo Compounds: Aliphatic and Aromatic Compounds, Interscience Publishers, Inc., New York, 1961.
   (c) B. I. BELOV and V. V. KOZLOV, *Usp. Khim.*, **32**, 121 (1963).
   (d) E. H. RODD, *Chemistry of Carbon Compounds*, vol. III-A, Elsevier Publishing Co., New York, 1954, p. 256.

2. J. M. INSOLE and E. S. LEWIS, *J. Am. Chem. Soc.*, **85**, 122 (1963); E. S. LEWIS and J. M. INSOLE, *ibid.*, **86**, 34, 107 (1964); see also R. A. ABRAMOVITCH *et al.*, *Tetrahedron Letters*, 1507 (1963); A. K. BOSE and I. KUGAJEVSKY, *J. Am. Chem. Soc.*, **88**, 2325 (1966).

3. (a) M. R. PIERCEY and E. R. WARD, *J. Chem. Soc.*, 3841 (1962).
   (b) I. UGI, in A. R. KATRITZKY, *Advances in Heterocyclic Chemistry*, vol. 3, Academic Press, New York, 1965, p. 373.

4. S. M. PARMERTER, in R. ADAMS, *Organic Reactions*, vol. 10, John Wiley and Sons, Inc., New York, 1959, p. 1.

5. R. R. PHILLIPS, in ref. 4, vol. 10 (1959), p. 143.

6. H. C. YAO and P. RESNICK, *J. Am. Chem. Soc.*, **84**, 3514 (1962).

7. M. STILES and A. SISTI, *J. Org. Chem.*, **25**, 1691 (1960); A. SISTI, J. BURGMASTER, and M. FUDIM, *ibid.*, **27**, 279 (1962); A. SISTI, J. SAWINSKI, and R. STOUT, *J. Chem. Eng. Data*, **9**, 108 (1964).

8. N. KORNBLUM, in ref. 4, vol. 2 (1944), p. 262.

9. H. ROE, in ref. 4, vol. 5 (1949), p. 193.

10. C. S. HAMILTON and J. F. MORGAN, in ref. 4, vol. 2 (1944), p. 415.

11. W. E. BACHMAN and R. A. HOFFMAN, in ref. 4, vol. 2 (1944), p. 224; see also J. I. G. CADOGAN, *J. Chem. Soc.*, 4257 (1962).

12. (a) C. S. RONDESTVEDT in ref. 4, vol. 11 (1960), p. 189.
    (b) R. KOELSCH and V. BOEKELHEIDE, *J. Am. Chem. Soc.*, **66**, 412 (1944); C. S. RONDESTVEDT, H. VOGL, *J. Am. Chem. Soc.*, **77**, 2313 (1955).

13. (a) L. I. SMITH, *Chem. Rev.*, **23**, 193 (1938).
    (b) B. EISTERT, in *Newer Methods of Preparative Organic Chemistry*, Interscience Publishers, Inc., New York, 1948, p. 513.
    (c) A. LEDWITH and E. C. FRIEDRICH, *J. Chem. Soc.*, 504 (1964).

14. S. R. PAULSEN, *Angew. Chem.*, **72**, 781 (1960).

15. E. SCHMITZ and R. OHME, *Chem. Ber.*, **94**, 2166 (1961).

16. E. SCHMITZ and R. OHME, *Tetrahedron Letters*, No. 17, 612 (1961); *Chem. Ber.*, **95**, 795 (1962); E. SCHMITZ, R. OHME, and R. D. SCHMIDT, *ibid.*, **95**, 2714 (1962); L. PIERCE and V. DOBYNS, *J. Am. Chem. Soc.*, **84**, 2657 (1962).

17. C. D. GUTSCHE, in ref. 4, vol. 8 (1954), p. 364.

18. T. J. DE BOER and H. J. BACKER, *Rec. Trav. Chim.*, **73**, 229 (1954); C. G. OVERBERGER and J-P. ANSELME, *J. Org. Chem.*, **28**, 592 (1963).

19. (a) W. R. BAMFORD and T. S. STEVENS, *J. Chem. Soc.*, 4735 (1952).
    (b) D. G. FARNUM, *J. Org. Chem.*, **28**, 870 (1963).

20. C. G. OVERBERGER, N. WEINSHENKER, and J-P. ANSELME, *J. Am. Chem. Soc.*, **87**, 4119 (1965).

21. J. MEINWALD, P. G. GASSMAN, and E. G. MILLER, *J. Am. Chem. Soc.*, **81**, 4757 (1959); W. RÜNDEL, *Angew. Chem.*, **74**, 592 (1963).

22. H. REIMLINGER, *Chem. Ber.*, **94**, 2547 (1961).

23. (a) E. MÜLLER, H. HAISS and W. RÜNDEL, *Chem. Ber.*, **93**, 1541 (1960).
    (b) W. RÜNDEL, *Angew. Chem.*, **76**, 603 (1964).

24. R. HUISGEN, *Angew. Chem.*, **67**, 439 (1955).

25. D. BETHELL and J. D. CALLISTER, *J. Chem. Soc.*, 3801, 3808 (1963).

26. (a) P. A. S. SMITH and D. R. BAER, in ref. 4, vol. 11 (1960), p. 157; for reactions with α,β-unsaturated ketones, see W. S. JOHNSON *et al.*, *J. Am. Chem. Soc.*, **84**, 989 (1962).
    (b) W. KIRMSE, *Chem. Ber.*, **93**, 2357 (1960).
    (c) P. T. IZZO and A. S. KENDE, *Chem. Ind. (London)*, 839 (1964); R. BRESLOW *et al.*, *J. Am. Chem. Soc.*, **87**, 1320 (1965); see also H. L. LOGOTHETIS, *J. Org. Chem.*, **29**, 3049 (1964).

27. M. S. NEWMAN and P. BEAL, *J. Am. Chem. Soc.*, **71**, 1506 (1949).

28. (a) F. WEYGAND and H. J. BESTMAN, *Angew. Chem.*, **72**, 532 (1960).
    (b) E. FAHR, *Angew. Chem.* **73**, 766 (1961).
    (c) A. MUSTAFA, *J. Chem. Soc.*, 234 (1949), G. D. BUCKLEY, *ibid.*, 1850 (1954); P. K. KADABA and J. O. EDWARDS, *J. Org. Chem.*, **26**, 233 (1961).

29. W. E. BACHMAN and W. S. STRUVE, in ref. 4, vol. 1 (1942), p. 38.

30. R. DIJKSTRA and H. J. BACKER, *Proc. Koninkl. Ned. Akad. Wetenschap.*, **55B**, 382 (1952).

31. H. J. BACKER and B. BOS, *Rec. Trav. Chim.*, **69**, 1233 (1950).

32. N. J. LEONARD, K. JANN, J. V. PAUKSTELIS, and C. K. STEINHARDT, *J. Org. Chem.*, **28**, 1499 (1963).

33. (a) E. FAHR, *Ann.*, **638**, 1 (1960); *Angew. Chem.*, **73**, 536 (1961).
    (b) E. FAHR and F. SCHECKENBACH, *Ann.*, **655**, 86 (1962); E. FAHR, K. DÖPPERT, and F. SCHECKENBACH, *Angew. Chem.*, **75**, 670 (1963).

34. E. GINSBURG *et al.*, *Dokl. Akad. Nauk SSSR*, **142**, 354 (1962).

35. R. HUISGEN, *Proc. Chem. Soc.*, 357 (1961); *Chem. Weekblad*, **59**, 89 (1963); *Angew. Chem.*, **75**, 604, 741 (1963); R. HUISGEN, R. GRASHEY, and J. SAUER, in S. PATAI, *The Chemistry of Alkenes*, John Wiley and Sons, Inc., New York, 1964, p. 739.

36. C. G. OVERBERGER and J-P. ANSELME, *J. Am. Chem. Soc.*, **84**, 869 (1962); **86**, 658 (1964).

37. R. HUISGEN, H. STANGL, H. J. STURM, and H. WAGENHOFER, *Angew. Chem.*, **73,** 170 (1961).

38. (a) T. V. VAN AUKEN and K. L. RINEHART, *J. Am. Chem. Soc.*, **84,** 3736 (1962); C. G. OVERBERGER, J-P. ANSELME, and J. R. HALL, *ibid.*, **85,** 2752 (1963).
   (b) C. G. OVERBERGER, N. WEINSHENKER, and J-P. ANSELME, *J. Am. Chem. Soc.*, **86,** 5364 (1964).

39. M. ALGUERO *et al.*, *Tetrahedron*, **18,** 1381 (1962); J. BASTUS, *Tetrahedron Letters*, 955 (1963); C. BELIL, J. PASCUAL, and F. SERRATOSA, *Anales Real Soc. Espan. Fis. Quim.*, *Ser. B*, **59,** 507 (1963).

40. G. L. CLOSS and J. J. COYLE, *J. Am. Chem. Soc.*, **84,** 4350 (1962).

41. H. REIMLINGER, *Angew. Chem.*, **74,** 153 (1962); H. REIMLINGER, F. BILLIAU, and M. PEIREN, *Chem. Ber.*, **97,** 339 (1964); see also A. SCHÖNBERG and E. FRESE, *Angew. Chem.*, **76,** 343 (1964).

42. (a) C. E. H. BAWN, *Proc. Chem. Sòc.*, 165 (1962), p. 174.
   (b) H. M. WHITLOCK, *J. Am. Chem. Soc.*, **84,** 2807 (1962).

43. A. M. READER and P. S. BAILEY, *Chem. Ind.* (*London*), 1620 (1961); A. M. READER, P. S. BAILEY, and H. M. WHITE, *J. Org. Chem.*, **30,** 784 (1965).

44. H. STAUDINGER and F. PFENNINGER, *Ber.*, **49,** 1941 (1916); L. V. VARGHA and E. KORAES, *ibid.*, **75,** 794 (1942); G. HESSE and S. MAJUMDAR, *Chem. Ber.*, **93,** 1129 (1960); see also G. OPITZ and K. FISCHER, *Angew. Chem.*, **77,** 41 (1965).

45. D. E. APPLEQUIST and H. BABAD, *J. Org. Chem.*, **27,** 288 (1962).

46. (a) G. WITTIG and M. SCHLÖSSER, *Tetrahedron*, **18,** 1023 (1962).
   (b) A. C. POSHKUS and J. E. HERWEH, *J. Org. Chem.*, **27,** 2700 (1962).

47. (a) W. R. BAMFORD and T. S. STEVENS. *J. Chem. Soc.*, 4675 (1952).
   (b) T. SEVERIN, *Angew. Chem.*, **70,** 745 (1958); *Chem. Ber.*, **92,** 1517 (1959).

48. D. G. FARNUM and P. YATES, *Proc. Chem. Soc.*, 224 (1960).

49. E. MÜLLER and W. RÜNDEL, *Chem. Ber.*, **90,** 2673 (1957); E. MÜLLER, P. KÄSTNER, and W. RÜNDEL; *ibid.*, **98,** 711 (1965); J-P. ANSELME, *J. Chem. Ed.*, **43** (1966).

50. P. MIGNINIAC, *Bull. Soc. Chim. France*, 2111 (1962); W. KIRMSE, *Angew. Chem.*, **71,** 537 (1959); **73,** 161 (1961); *Carbene Chemistry*, Academic Press, New York, 1964; E. CHINOPOROS, *Chem. Rev.*, **63,** 235 (1963); I. L. KNUNYANTS, N. P. GAMBARYAN, and E. M. ROHLIN, *Usp. Khim.*, **27,** 1361 (1958); J. HINE, *Divalent Carbon*, The Ronald Press Co., New York, 1964.

51. W. SCHLENK and C. BORNHARDT, *Ann.*, **394,** 183 (1912); see also E. MÜLLER, A. MOOSMAYER, and A. RIECHER, *Z. Naturforsch*, **18b,** 982 (1963).

52. C. RÜCHARDT and G. N. SCHRANZER, *Chem. Ber.*, **93,** 1840 (1960).

53. (a) L. HORNER, L. HOCKENBERGER, and W. KIRMSE, *Chem. Ber.*, **94,** 290 (1961).
   (b) E. FAHR and H. LIND, *Angew. Chem.*, **75,** 1122 (1963).
   (c) A. GUILLEMONAT, in V. GRIGNARD (ed.) *Traité de Chimie Organique*, vol. 15, Masson et Cie, Paris, 1948, p. 25.

54. T. KAUFFMAN and S. M. HAGE, *Angew. Chem.*, **75,** 248 (1963).

55. M. Z. BARAKAT, M. F. A. EL-WAHAB and M. M. EL-SADR, *J. Am. Chem. Soc.*, **77,** 1670 (1955).

56. D. H. R. BARTON, R. E. O'BRIEN, and S. STERNHELL, *J. Chem. Soc.*, 470 (1962).

57. N. LATIF and I. FATHY, *J. Org. Chem.*, **24,** 1883 (1959).

58. H. E. ZIMMERMAN and S. SOMASEKHARA, *J. Am. Chem. Soc.*, **82,** 5865 (1960).

59. F. S. BRIDSON-JONES *et al.*, *J. Chem. Soc.*, 2999, 3009, 3016 (1951).

60. L. HORNER, W. KIRMSE, and H. FERNEKESS, *Chem. Ber.*, **94,** 279 (1961); L. HORNER and H. FERNEKESS, *ibid.*, **94,** 712 (1961).

61. C. G. OVERBERGER and J-P. ANSELME, *Tetrahedron Letters*, 1405 (1963); see also E. SCHMITZ, A. STARK, and C. HÖNIG, *Chem. Ber.*, **98,** 2509 (1965).

62. J. P. WIBAUT and J. W. P. BOON, *Helv. Chim. Acta*, **44,** 1171 (1961); R. E. MILLER, *J. Org. Chem.*, **26,** 2327 (1961).

63. C. PEDERSEN, *Acta Chim. Scand.*, **12**, 1236 (1960).

64. H. E. BAUMGARTEN and C. H. ANDERSON, *J. Am. Chem. Soc.*, **83**, 399 (1961).

65. H. U. DAENIKER and J. DRUEY, *Helv. Chim. Acta*, **46**, 805 (1962).

66. G. L. CLOSS and W. BOLL, *Angew. Chem.*, **75**, 640 (1963); G. L. CLOSS, L. E. CLOSS, and W. BOLL, *J. Am. Chem. Soc.*, **85**, 3796 (1963); G. L. CLOSS and W. BOLL, *ibid.*, **85**, 1904 (1963); G. EGE, *Tetrahedron Letters*, 1665, 1667 (1963).

67. R. FUSCO, G. BIANCHETTI, D. POCAR, and R. UGO, *Chem. Ber.*, **96**, 802 (1963); P. GRÜNANGER and P. V. FINZI, *Tetrahedron Letters*, 1053 (1963).

68. (a) J. S. SPLITTER and M. CALVIN, *J. Org. Chem.*, **23**, 651 (1958).
    (b) R. BONNETT, V. M. CLARK, and A. TODD, *J. Chem. Soc.*, 2012 (1959).

69. C. J. PEDERSEN, *J. Am. Chem. Soc.*, **79**, 5014 (1957).

70. (a) W. H. GRAHAM, *J. Am. Chem. Soc.*, **84**, 1063 (1962).
    (b) W. H. GRAHAM, unpublished results.

71. (a) G. C. PIMENTEL and C. B. MOORE, unpublished results.
    (b) M. J. AMRICH and J. A. BELL, *J. Am. Chem. Soc.*, **86**, 292 (1954).

72. G. W. WHELAND, *Advanced Organic Chemistry*, John Wiley and Sons, Inc., New York, 1960, p. 728.

73. E. SCHMITZ, *Angew. Chem.*, **76**, 197 (1964).

74. C. G. OVERBERGER and J-P. ANSELME, *J. Org. Chem.*, **29**, 1188 (1964).

75. H. M. FREY and I. D. R. STEVENS, *Proc. Chem. Soc.*, 79 (1962); *J. Am. Chem. Soc.*, **84**, 2547 (1962); *J. Chem. Soc.*, 3865 (1962); 3514 (1963); 4700 (1964); 1700 (1965).

76. D. M. GALE, W. J. MIDDLETON, and C. G. KRESPAN, *J. Am. Chem. Soc.*, **87**, 657 (1965).

6

Hydrazides

6–1. INTRODUCTION

Hydrazides are derivatives of hydrazines having one or more "acyl" substituents on the nitrogen atoms. Under the generic name "acyl" are included such groups as RCO—, RSO_2—, $R'OCO$—, etc. For purposes of discussion, hydrazides will be classified as

1. Monoacylhydrazides: Acyl-NRNR'R"
2. 1,2-Diacylhydrazides: Acyl-NR—NR'-acyl

All the compounds discussed will be considered as derivatives of those two classes.

6–2. PREPARATION

Monoacylhydrazides

Simple monoacylhydrazides are usually prepared by the reaction of the corresponding ester with an excess of hydrazine:

$$RCOOC_2H_5 + H_2NNH_2 \rightarrow RCONHNH_2 + C_2H_5OH \tag{6–1}$$

This method becomes less valuable as the residue on the ester (R—) increases in size. In these cases, it may be necessary to use the more reactive acyl halide, although this procedure usually gives the 1,2-diacylderivative (see 6–3). Monosulfonyl hydrazides are prepared by the reaction of the sulfonyl halide with hydrazine. Interaction of acylamides with hydrazine is also useful in preparing monoacylhydrazides. The salt first obtained by the addition of hydrazine to an acid gives the monoacylhydrazide upon pyrolysis. 1,1-Disubstituted acyl hydrazides can be obtained by the reaction with the acid halides:

$$\begin{matrix} R' \\ \diagdown \\ N-NH_2 + RCOCl \rightarrow RCO-NHN \\ \diagup \\ R'' \end{matrix} \qquad \begin{matrix} R' \\ \diagup \\ \diagdown \\ R'' \end{matrix} \tag{6–2}$$

'1,2-Diacylhydrazides

As was previously mentioned, the reaction of acyl halides with hydrazine gives excellent yields of the 1,2-diacylhydrazides, which can also be prepared by the oxidation of the corresponding monoacylhydrazide:

$$2 \text{ RCOCl} + \text{H}_2\text{NNH}_2 \rightarrow \text{RCONHNHCOR} \qquad (6\text{-}3)$$

$$2 \text{ RCONHNH}_2 + \text{I}_2 \rightarrow \text{RCONHNHCOR} \qquad (6\text{-}4)$$

"Mixed" 1,2-diacylhydrazides are obtained by the reaction of monacyl-hydrazides with the appropriate acyl halides:

$$\text{RCONHNH}_2 + \text{ArSO}_2\text{Cl} \rightarrow \text{RCONHNHSO}_2\text{Ar} \qquad (6\text{-}5)$$

Methods for the introduction of the carbo-*t*-butoxy group have been developed largely through the efforts of Carpino.[1]

It was recently found that the carbo-*t*-butoxy group can be smoothly removed from hydrazines by pyrolysis.[2] This reaction proceeding probably via a six-membered transition state, offers promise as an alternative method for the removal of the carbo-*t*-butoxy group:

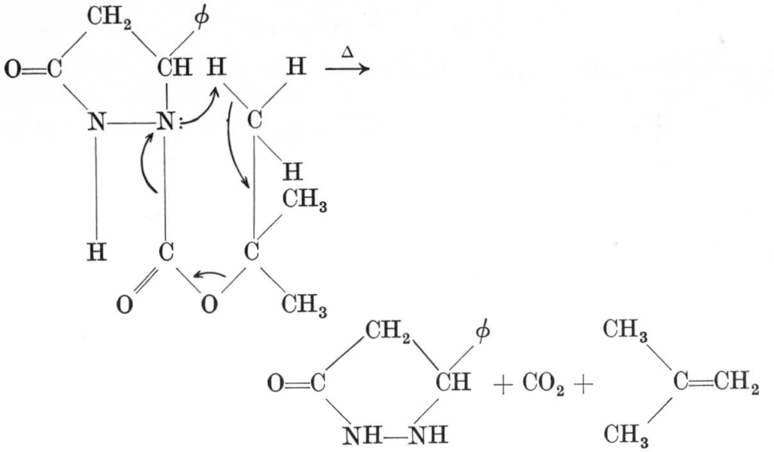

6-3. REACTIONS

Monoacylhydrazides

General. Monoacylhydrazides are used as an alternative route for the preparation of acylazides. Sodium nitrite is used most often as the nitro-sating agent, although alkyl nitrites have seen some applications.

Semicarbazide is well known as a "carbonyl reagent," but most hydrazides react similarly. The catalytic reduction of hydrazides in the presence of Raney nickel results in the cleavage of the nitrogen-nitrogen bond.[3] It has been previously mentioned (see 6-4) that monoacylhydrazides can be oxidized to 1,2-diacylhydrazides.   The use of peracetic acid for such oxidations has been recently reported.[4]

The alkylation of monoacylhydrazides proceeds with attack of the "non-acyl" nitrogen.   A second alkylating group also will enter at the same nitrogen and even 1,1-dialkyl-2-acylhydrazides will be alkylated to give hydrazidinium salts:

$$RCONHNH_2 + 2\ R'X \longrightarrow RCONHNR'_2 \xrightarrow{R'X}$$

$$RCONH\overset{+}{N}R'_3 \xrightarrow{base} RCO\overset{-}{N}\!\!-\!\!\overset{+}{N}R'_3 \quad (6\text{-}7)$$
$$X^- \qquad\qquad\quad \overset{..}{I}$$

These hydrazidinium salts will, in the presence of base, give "ylid" (I) type compounds.[5]   Hydrazides can be reduced by mixed hydrides to the corresponding hydrazines.

Reactions With Loss of Nitrogen.   Under this heading are collected reactions in which the eventual result of the reaction consists in the replacement of the "hydrazide residue" of monoacylhydrazides:

The Kalb-Gross oxidation to aldehydes:[6]

$$RCONHNH_2 \xrightarrow{[O],\,base} R\!\!-\!\!CHO \qquad\qquad (6\text{-}8)$$

The Carpino conversion to acylhalides:[7,8]

$$RCONHNH_2 \xrightarrow{HCl,\,2\,Cl_2} RCOCl + N_2 + 3\ HCl \qquad (6\text{-}9)$$

$$ArSO_2NHNH_2 \xrightarrow{2\,Br_2} ArSO_2Br + N_2 + 3\ HBr \qquad (6\text{-}10)$$

An essentially similar reaction has been used by Wolman and Gallop for peptide synthesis.[9]

The Nickon-Sinz deamination:[10]

$$RNH_2 + R'SO_2Cl \rightarrow RNHSO_2R' \xrightarrow{NH_2OSO_3H}$$

$$R\!\!-\!\!\underset{\underset{NH_2}{|}}{N}\!\!-\!\!SO_2R' \rightarrow RH + R'SO_2H + N_2 \quad (6\text{-}11)$$

Aryl hydrazides are cleaved by base to the corresponding hydrocarbons:

$$ArNHNHSO_2R \xrightarrow{NaOH} ArH + N_2 + RSO_3H \qquad (6\text{-}12)$$

The decomposition of sulfonylhydrazides; diimide:

$$ArSO_2NHNH_2 \xrightarrow{\Delta} ArSO_2H + [HN\!\!=\!\!NH] \qquad (6\text{-}13)$$

Alkyl azides from hydrazides:[11]

$$R\!\!-\!\!\underset{\underset{NH_2}{|}}{N}\!\!-\!\!CONH_2 \xrightarrow{HONO} RN_3 + CO_2 + N_2 \qquad (6\text{-}14)$$

α,β-Unsaturated acids from pyrazolinones:[12a]

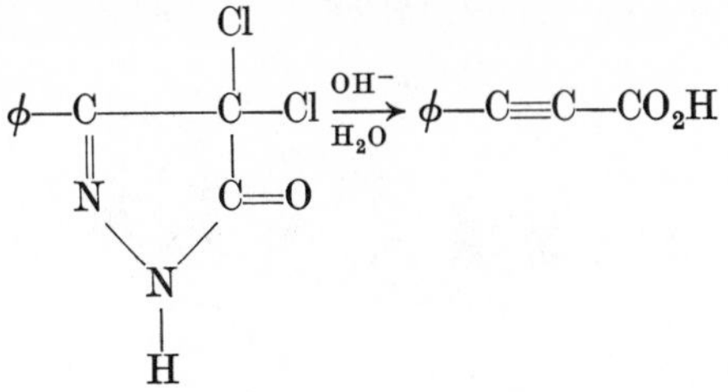

$$\phi-C\underset{\substack{\displaystyle \| \\ N}}{\overset{\substack{\displaystyle Cl \\ |}}{}}\;\;C\underset{\substack{\displaystyle | \\ C=O}}{\overset{\substack{\displaystyle Cl \\ |}}{}}Cl \;\xrightarrow[\text{H}_2\text{O}]{\text{OH}^-}\; \phi-C\equiv C-CO_2H \qquad (6\text{--}15a)$$

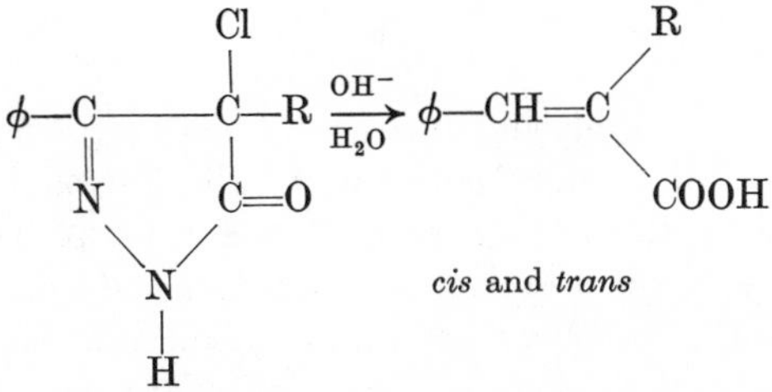

(ring N—N—H)

$$\phi-C\underset{\substack{\displaystyle \| \\ N}}{}\;\;C\underset{\substack{\displaystyle | \\ C=O}}{\overset{\substack{\displaystyle Cl \\ |}}{}}R \;\xrightarrow[\text{H}_2\text{O}]{\text{OH}^-}\; \phi-CH=C\overset{\displaystyle R}{\underset{\displaystyle COOH}{}} \qquad (6\text{--}15b)$$

cis and *trans*

It has been recently shown that these reactions proceed via a diazacyclopentadienone intermediate.[12a]

Olefins from dihydrooxadiazinones:[12b]

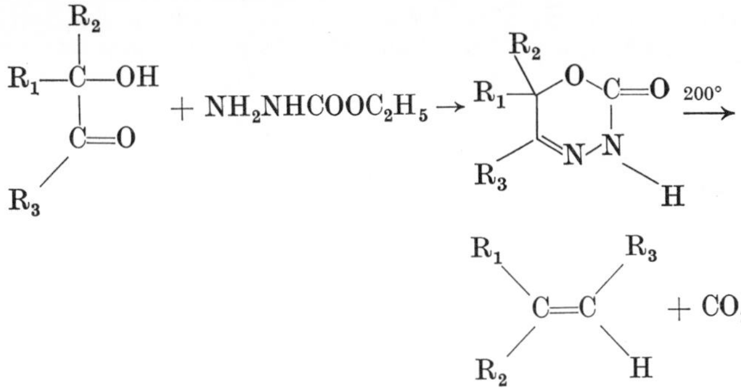

$$R_1-\underset{\substack{\displaystyle | \\ C=O \\ / \\ R_3}}{\overset{\substack{\displaystyle R_2 \\ |}}{C}}-OH \;+\; NH_2NHCOOC_2H_5 \;\rightarrow\; R_1\underset{\substack{\displaystyle \| \\ R_3}}{\overset{\substack{\displaystyle R_2 \\ }}{}}\;\overset{O\diagdown}{\underset{N-N}{}}C=O \;\;\xrightarrow{200°}$$

$$\underset{\substack{\displaystyle / \\ R_2}}{\overset{\substack{\displaystyle R_1 \\ \diagdown}}{C}}=\underset{\substack{\displaystyle \diagdown \\ H}}{\overset{\substack{\displaystyle R_3 \\ /}}{C}} \;+\; CO_2 + N_2 \qquad (6\text{--}16)$$

The Bamford-Stevens conversion of tosylhydrazones to diazoalkanes (Chapters 3 and 5) as well as the analogous base catalyzed decomposition of 1,1-disubstituted tosylhydrazides reported by Carpino[13] (Chapters 2 and 7) have been discussed. The reduction of tosylhydrazones by means of lithium aluminum hydride (LAH) to the saturated hydrocarbons[14] provides a useful alternative to the Wolff-Kishner reaction:

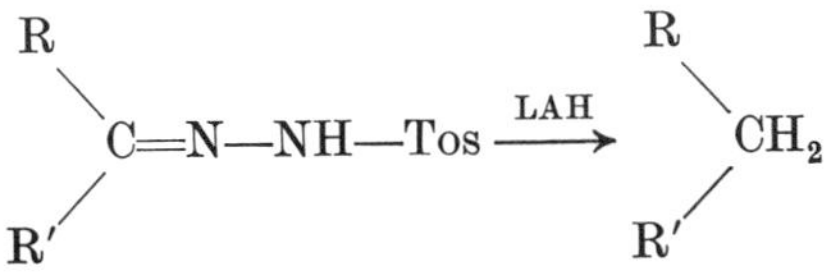

$$\underset{\substack{\displaystyle / \\ R'}}{\overset{\substack{\displaystyle R \\ \diagdown}}{C}}=N-NH-Tos \;\xrightarrow{\text{LAH}}\; \underset{\substack{\displaystyle / \\ R'}}{\overset{\substack{\displaystyle R \\ \diagdown}}{C}}H_2 \qquad (6\text{--}17)$$

The formation of the interesting pyrazolenines (II) from the salts of tosyl-hydrazones of α,β-unsaturated carbonyl compounds has been recently reported:[15]

$$
\begin{array}{c}
\text{R}\qquad\text{R}'' \\
\diagdown\quad\diagup \\
\text{C}\!=\!\text{C}\!-\!\text{C}\!=\!\text{N}\!-\!\overset{-}{\underset{..}{\text{N}}}\!-\!\text{Tos} \\
\diagup\quad\diagdown \\
\text{R}'\qquad\text{R}''' \\
\text{Na}^+
\end{array}
\xrightarrow{\Delta}
\qquad
\text{II}
\qquad (6\text{-}18)
$$

1,2-Diacylhydrazides

The alkylation of 1,2-diacylhydrazides provides a convenient method for the preparation of 1,2-dialkylhydrazines. The scope of the McFadyen-Stevens aldehyde synthesis[16] has been extended to aliphatic aldehydes[17] by the use of dimethylsulfoxide as a reaction medium, and a modified mechanism (similar to that of the Hoffman reaction) for the reaction has been suggested[18] (6-19):

$$
\text{RCO}\!-\!\text{NHNH}\!-\!\text{SO}_2\text{Ar} \xrightarrow{\text{base}} \text{RCONH}\overset{-}{\text{N}}\!\!\frown\!\!\text{SO}_2\text{Ar} \longrightarrow
$$

$$
\text{RCONH}\!-\!\underset{..}{\text{N}} \rightleftharpoons [\text{RCO}\!-\!\text{N}\!=\!\text{N}\!-\!\text{H}] \quad (6\text{-}19)
$$

Five-membered ring heterocycles are easily formed from 1,2-diacyl-hydrazides; e.g. the formation of 2,5-diphenyl-1,3,4-oxadiazole (III) from dibenzoylhydrazine:

$$
\begin{array}{c}
\overset{\text{O}}{\overset{\|}{}}\qquad\overset{\text{O}}{\overset{\|}{}} \\
\phi\!-\!\text{C}\!-\!\text{NHNH}\!-\!\text{C}\!-\!\phi \xrightarrow{\text{P}_2\text{O}_5} \phi\!-\!\text{C}\underset{\text{O}}{\overset{\text{N}-\text{N}}{\diagup\diagdown}}\text{C}\!-\!\phi
\end{array}
\qquad (6\text{-}20)
$$

III

Thiadiazoles and triazoles can be similarly prepared. With phosphorous pentachloride, 1,2-diacylhydrazides can be converted to α,α'-bischloroazines:

$$
\begin{array}{c}
\overset{\text{O}}{\overset{\|}{}}\quad\overset{\text{O}}{\overset{\|}{}} \\
\text{R}\!-\!\text{CNHNHC}\!-\!\text{R}
\end{array}
\xrightarrow{2\ \text{PCl}_5}
\begin{array}{c}
\overset{\text{Cl}}{\overset{|}{}}\qquad\overset{\text{Cl}}{\overset{|}{}} \\
\text{R}\!-\!\text{C}\!=\!\text{N}\!-\!\text{N}\!=\!\text{C}\!-\!\text{R}
\end{array}
+ 2\ \text{HCl} + 2\ \text{POCl}_3 \quad (6\text{-}21)
$$

Diacylhydrazides are easily oxidized to the corresponding azodiacyls,[35] which are excellent dienophiles,[19] giving six-membered tetrahydropyridazine derivatives:

$$
\text{RCO}\!-\!\text{NHNH}\!-\!\text{COR} \xrightarrow{[\text{O}]} \text{RCON}\!=\!\text{NCOR} \xrightarrow{\text{butadiene}}
\begin{array}{c}
\overset{\text{N}-\text{COR}}{} \\
\overset{|}{} \\
\overset{\text{N}-\text{COR}}{}
\end{array}
\qquad (6\text{-}22)
$$

One example of a four-membered ring formation with an olefin is that with tetrafluoroethylene:[20]

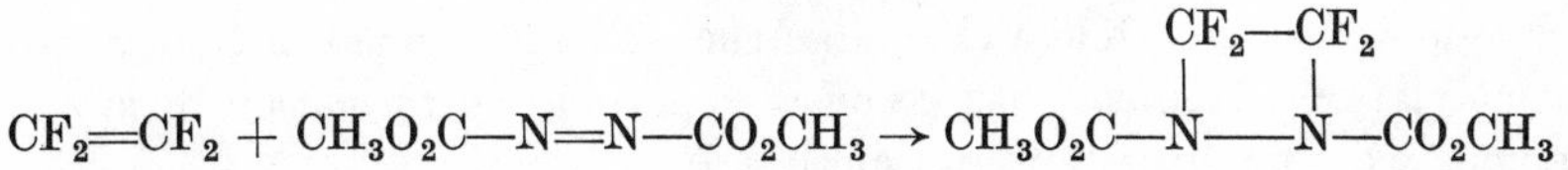

$$CF_2{=}CF_2 + CH_3O_2C{-}N{=}N{-}CO_2CH_3 \rightarrow CH_3O_2C{-}N\overset{\overset{\displaystyle CF_2{-}CF_2}{|\qquad|}}{\underline{\qquad}}N{-}CO_2CH_3$$

$$(6\text{--}23)$$

However, substitution reactions can occur when there is a labile hydrogen. Some of the more interesting examples are given below:

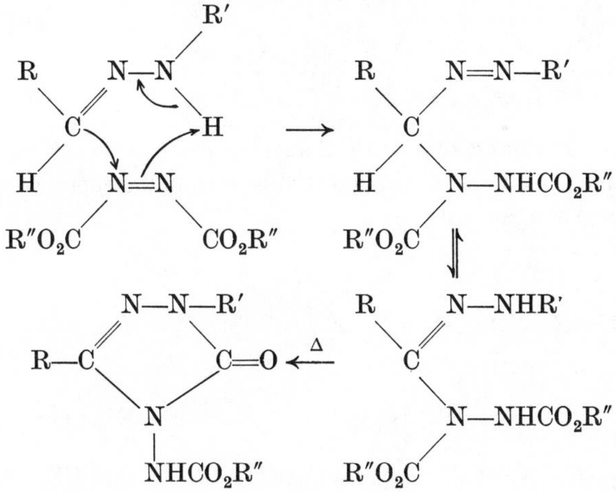

$$(6\text{--}24)^{[21]}$$

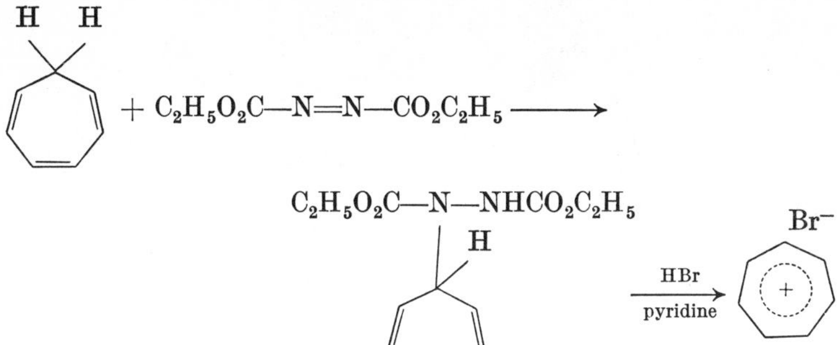

$$(6\text{--}25)^{[22]}$$

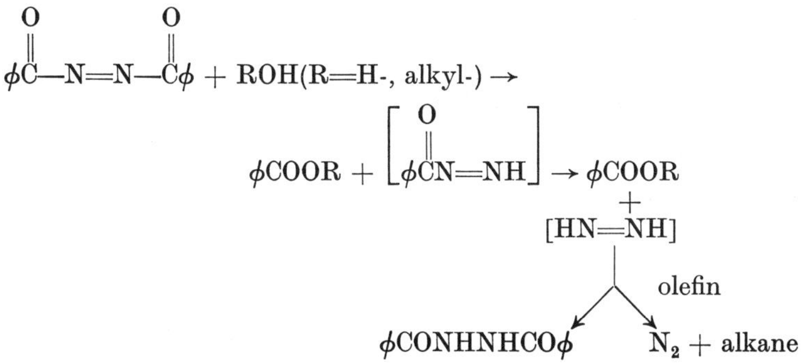

$$\phi\overset{\overset{\displaystyle O}{\|}}{C}{-}N{=}N{-}\overset{\overset{\displaystyle O}{\|}}{C}\phi + ROH(R{=}H\text{-, alkyl-}) \rightarrow$$

$$\phi COOR + \left[\phi\overset{\overset{\displaystyle O}{\|}}{C}N{=}NH \right] \rightarrow \phi COOR$$

$$+ \\ [HN{=}NH]$$

$$(6\text{--}26)^{[23]}$$

olefin

$$\phi CONHNHCO\phi \qquad N_2 + \text{alkane}$$

t-Butylmagnesium iodide adds across the —N=N— bond of *t*-butyl azodicarboxylate.[24] Hoffman has recently reported the formation of aryl carbanions via a potentially useful method:[25]

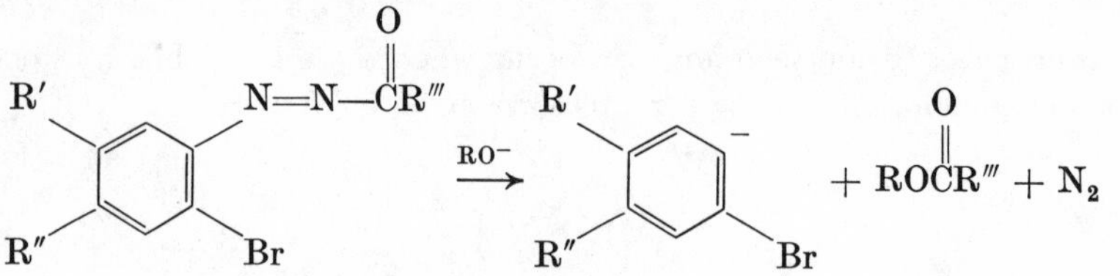

(6–27)

The reaction of azodiesters with diazoalkanes was briefly mentioned in Chapter 5 (see 5–36), and the mechanism is sufficiently complicated to warrant some thought:

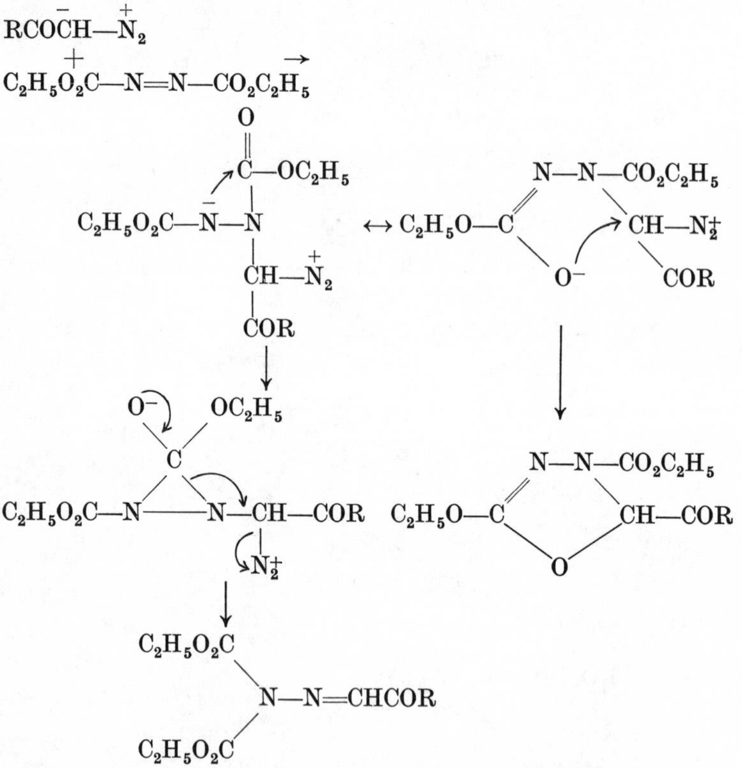

(6–28)

With diazonium salts, 1,2-diacylhydrazides give hexazadienes:[26]

$$ArN_2^+\,Cl^- + RCONHNHCOR \rightarrow Ar{-}N{=}N{-}N(COR){-}N(COR){-}N{=}N{-}Ar \qquad (6\text{–}29)$$

N,N'-Dialkoxy-1,2-diacylhydrazides, prepared by the oxidation of N-carbalkoxy-O-alkylhydroxylamines with silver oxide, exhibit unusual reactions in the presence of acids and bases.[27]

Rearrangements

The variety of functional groups that may be present in hydrazides leads to usual rearrangements. A few examples of the more interesting ones will be mentioned.

Distillation of N-benzyl-N,N-dimethylacetimides (IV) results in the migration of the benzyl groups:[28]

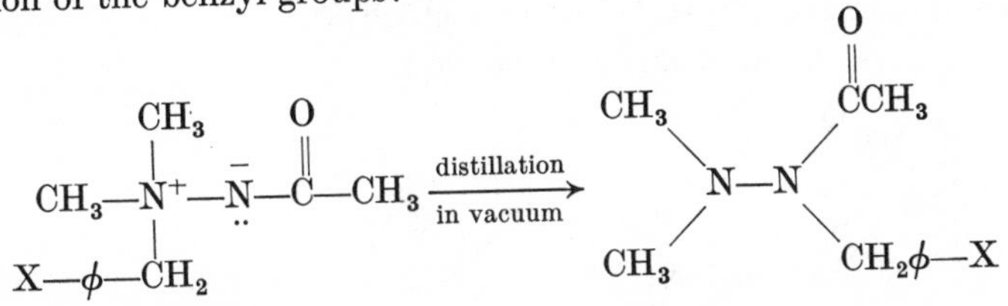

$$(6\text{--}30)$$

It was recently shown[29] that under acid conditions the reactions of 1-methyl- , 1,1-dimethyl- , and 1,1-dibenzyl-2-tosylhydrazines undergo prior dissociation into diazenium (V) and sulfinate ions:

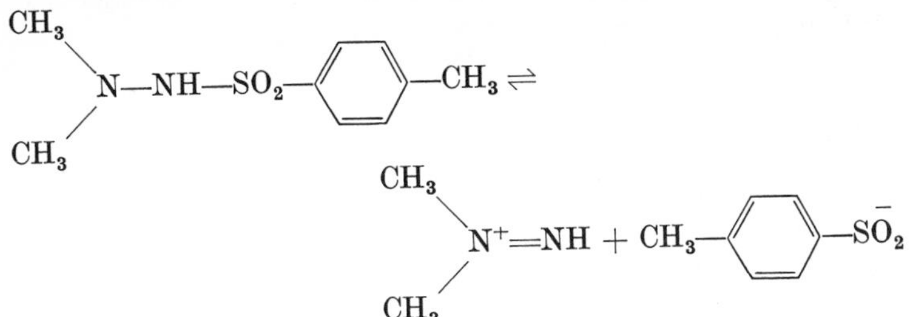

$$(6\text{--}31)$$

The products are those derived from these two species. The question of the existence of diazenium ion will be discussed in Chapter 7.

The base-catalyzed rearrangement of 2-allyl-2-benzenesulfonyl benzhydrazide to 3-benzenesulfonylpropanal benzhydrazone proceeds via an elimination-addition mechanism:[30]

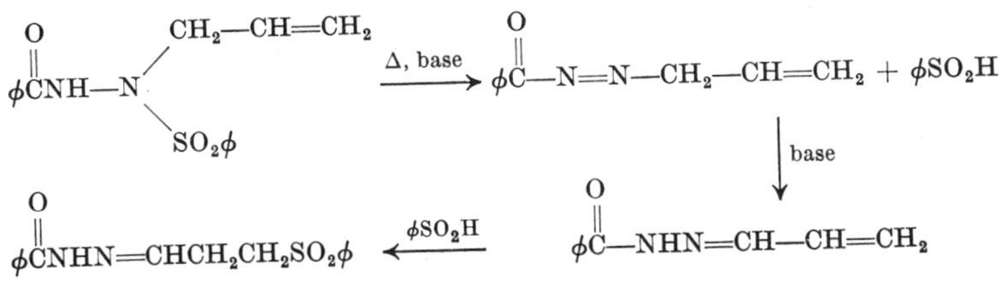

$$(6\text{--}32)$$

The rearranged product (VI) is the main product of the acid hydrolysis of the adduct from the reaction of diphenylketene with 2-carbethoxyazobenzene:[31]

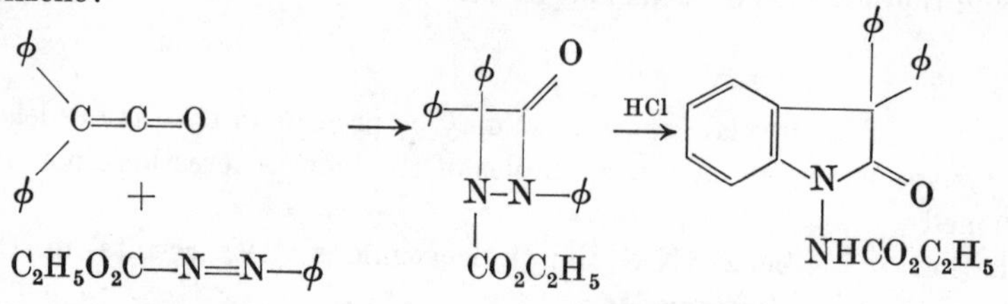

$$(6\text{-}33)$$

The rearrangement of α-N-acetyl-L-tyrosinhydrazide offers promise as a new method of identification of certain α-amino acids:[32]

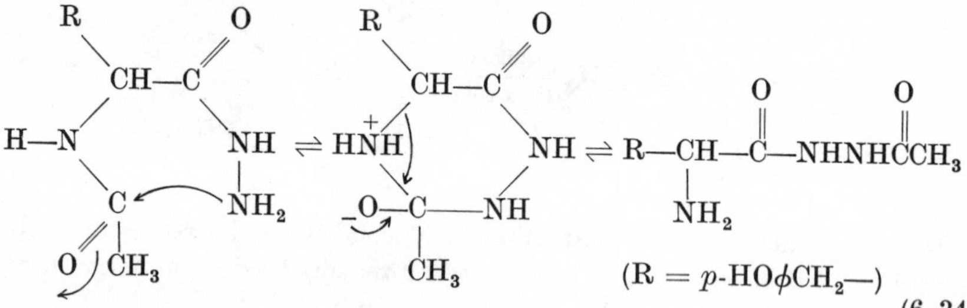

$$(R = p\text{-}HO\phi CH_2\text{—})$$

$$(6\text{-}34)$$

An extension of the lead tetraacetate oxidation of hydrazones led to interesting results:[33]

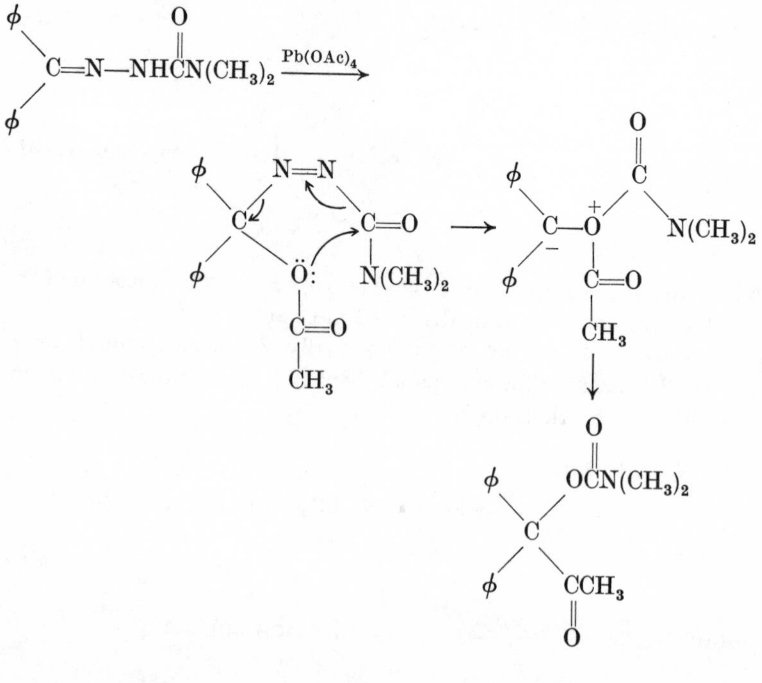

$$(6\text{-}35)$$

The base-catalyzed rearrangement of 2-benzyl-2-phenyl tosylhydrazide has been pictured as involving a "nitrene" intermediate[34] (see Chapter 7):

$$[\phi\cdot + \phi CH_2\cdot] \quad (6\text{–}36)$$

products

REFERENCES

General

H. WIELAND, *Die Hydrazine*, Verlag F. Enke, Stuttgart, 1913, p. 180.

C. C. CLARK, *Hydrazine*, Mathieson Chemical Corp., Baltimore, 1953, p. 43.

Text

1. L. A. CARPINO, *J. Am. Chem. Soc.*, **82**, 2725 (1960); *J. Org. Chem.*, **28**, 1909 (1963). **29**, 2820 (1964).

2. C. G. OVERBERGER, N. WEINSHENKER, and J-P. ANSELME, unpublished results.

3. C. AINSWORTH, *J. Am. Chem. Soc.*, **76**, 5774 (1954); **78**, 1636 (1956); R. L. HINMAN, *ibid.*, **78**, 2463 (1956); *J. Org. Chem.*, **22**, 148 (1957); T. UEDA and T. TSUJU, *Chem. Pharm. Bull. (Tokyo)*, **9**, 71 (1961).

4. L. HORNER and H. FERNEKESS, *Chem., Ber.* **94**, 712 (1961).

5. H. H. SISLER, G. M. OMIETANSKI, and B. RUDNER, *Chem. Rev.*, **57**, 1021 (1957); R. L. HINMAN and M. C. FLORES, *J. Org. Chem.*, **24**, 660 (1959).

6. E. MOSETTIG, in R. ADAMS, *Organic Reactions*, vol. 8, John Wiley and Sons, Inc., New York, 1954, p. 233.

7. L. A. CARPINO, *J. Am. Chem. Soc.*, **79**, 98 (1957).

8. A. C. POSHKUS, J. E. HERWEH, and F. A. MAGNOTTA, *J. Org. Chem.*, **28**, 2766 (1963).

9. Y. WOLMAN, P. M. GALLOP, H. PATCHORNICK, and A. BERGER, *J. Am. Chem. Soc.*, **83**, 1263 (1961); **84**, 1889 (1962); Y. WOLMAN and P. M. GALLOP, *J. Org. Chem.*, **27**, 1902 (1962); D. M. BROWN and N. K. KRAMER, *Proc. Chem. Soc.*, 212 (1960).

10. A. NICKON and A. SINZ, *J. Am. Chem. Soc.*, **82**, 753 (1960); A. NICKON and A. S. HILL, *ibid.*, **86**, 1152 (1964).

11. P. A. S. SMITH, J. M. CLEGG, and S. LAKRITZ, *J. Org. Chem.*, **23**, 1595 (1958).

12. (a) L. A. CARPINO, *J. Am. Chem. Soc.*, **80**, 599, 601 (1958); L. A. CARPINO, P. H. TERRY, and S. D. THATTE *Tetrahedron Letters*, 2329 (1964).
(b) M. ROSENBLUM *et al.*, *Chem. Ind. (London)*, 1480 (1956); *J. Am. Chem. Soc.*, **85**, 3874 (1963).

13. L. A. CARPINO, *J. Am. Chem. Soc.*, **79**, 4427 (1957).

14. L. CAGLIOTTI and M. MAGI, *Tetrahedron*, **19**, 1127 (1963).

15. G. L. CLOSS and W. BOLL, *Angew. Chem.*, **75**, 640 (1963); see also ref. 66 of Chapter 5.

16. Ref. 6, p. 232.

17. L. FRIEDMAN, American Chemical Society Abstracts, Fall 1962 Meeting, p. 96-Q, no. 174; see also M. SPRECHER, M. FELDKINEL, and M. WILCHEK, *J. Org. Chem.*, **26**, 3664 (1961).

18. U. M. BROWN, P. H. CARTER, and M. TOMLINSON, *J. Chem. Soc.*, 1843 (1958).

19. S. B. NEEDLEMAN and M. C. CHANG KUO, *Chem. Rev.*, **62**, 405 (1862).

20. J. C. KAUER and H. F. SCHNEIDER, *J. Am. Chem. Soc.*, **82**, 852 (1960); R. W. HOFFMANN and H. HÄUSER, *Angew. Chem.*, **76**, 346 (1964).

21. B. T. GILLIS and F. A. DANISHER, *J. Org. Chem.*, **27**, 4001 (1962).

22. J. M. CINNAMON and K. WEISS, *ibid.*, **26**, 2644 (1961).

23. J. F. NEUMER and J. T. GERIG, American Chemical Society Abstracts, Fall 1962 Meeting p. 23-Q, no. 40. J. E. LEFFLER and W. B. BOND, *J. Am. Chem. Soc.*, **78**, 335 (1956); D. MACKAY, U. F. MARK, and W. A. WATERS, *J. Chem. Soc.*, 4793 (1964); S. G. COHEN and J. NICHOLSON, *J. Org. Chem.*, **30**, 1162 (1965).

24. L. A. CARPINO, P. H. TERRY, and P. J. CROWLEY, *J. Org. Chem.*, **26**, 4336 (1961).

25. R. W. HOFFMANN, *Angew. Chem.*, **75**, 168 (1963); *Chem. Ber.*, **97**, 2763, 2772 (1964).

26. J. P. HORWITZ and V. A. GRAKAUSAS, *J. Am. Chem. Soc.*, **79**, 1249 (1957).

27. R. J. CRAWFORD and R. RAAP, *J. Org. Chem.* **28**, 2419 (1963).

28. S. WAWZONEK and E. YEAKEY, *J. Am. Chem. Soc.*, **82**, 5718 (1960).

29. S. WAWZONEK and W. McKILLIP, *J. Org. Chem.*, **27**, 3946 (1962).

30. M. S. NEWMAN and I. UNGAR, *J. Org. Chem.*, **27**, 1238 (1962).

31. C. W. BIRD, *J. Chem. Soc.*, 674 (1963); 5284 (1964).

32. A. N. KURTZ and C. NIEMANN, *J. Am. Chem. Soc.*, **83**, 3309 (1961).

33. D. C. IFFLAND and T. M. DAVIS, *ibid.*, **85**, 2182 (1963).

34. P. CARTER and T. S. STEVENS, *J. Chem. Soc.*, **1743** (1961); D. LEMAL, F. MENGER and E. COATS, *J. Am. Chem. Soc.*, **86**, 2395 (1964).

35. E. FAHR and H. LIND, *Angew. Chem.*, **78**, 376 (1966).

7

N-Nitrosamines

7-1. INTRODUCTION

N-Nitrosamines (I), as the name indicates, have the nitroso function directly bonded to the nitrogen atom of the amine residue:

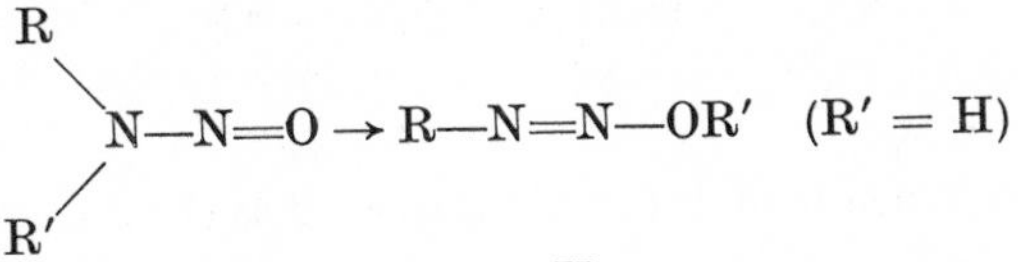

$$\begin{array}{c} R \\ \diagdown \\ N\!-\!N\!=\!O \rightarrow R\!-\!N\!=\!N\!-\!OR' \quad (R' = H) \\ \diagup \\ R' \\ \text{I} \text{II} \end{array}$$

In general, when cne of the substituents of the amine is hydrogen, the tautomeric form (II) is favored as in the oxime form of the C-nitroso compounds. The diazohydroxides are not stable and are the products first formed during the nitrosation of primary amines (see Chapter 5, 7, and 8). The parent compound (R = R' = H) is not known. The chemistry of N-nitrosamines will therefore be circumscribed to those in which neither R nor R' is hydrogen.

7-2. PREPARATION

The most general and most practical preparation of N-nitrosamines consists in the addition of sodium nitrite to a slightly acid solution of the secondary amine. The pH must be so adjusted that the nitrosonium ion is generated in the presence of enough free amine to permit the reaction to occur. When this method is not practical because of the structural features of the amines, "nitrous fumes" (or better nitrosyl chloride) have been advantageously utilized as the nitrosating agent. In certain cases, the use of carbon tetranitrite is of interest:

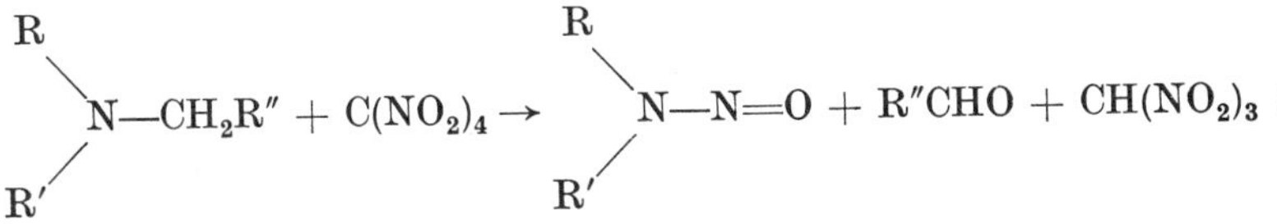

$$\begin{array}{c} R \\ \diagdown \\ N\!-\!CH_2R'' + C(NO_2)_4 \rightarrow \\ \diagup \\ R' \end{array} \qquad \begin{array}{c} R \\ \diagdown \\ N\!-\!N\!=\!O + R''CHO + CH(NO_2)_3 \quad (7\text{-}1) \\ \diagup \\ R' \end{array}$$

Tetraarylhydrazines react with nitric oxide to give the corresponding N-nitrosamines; with oxime salts, nitric oxide forms the N-nitroso salts.[1]   A useful synthesis of azoxy compounds makes use of the reaction of Grignard reagents with the O-tosyl derivatives of N-nitrosohydroxylamines.[1b]   N-Nitrosoarylamides can alternatively be prepared by the reaction of the acyl halide with the salt of aryldiazohydroxides.

7-3. REACTIONS

Several methods have been used to reduce N-nitrosbamines to the corresponding 1,1-disubstituted hydrazines. The tetrazenes are sometimes formed in small amounts. The action of potassium hydroxide on aryl alkyl N-nitrosamines gives the salt of the aryldiazohydroxide and the alcohol corresponding to the alkyl group:

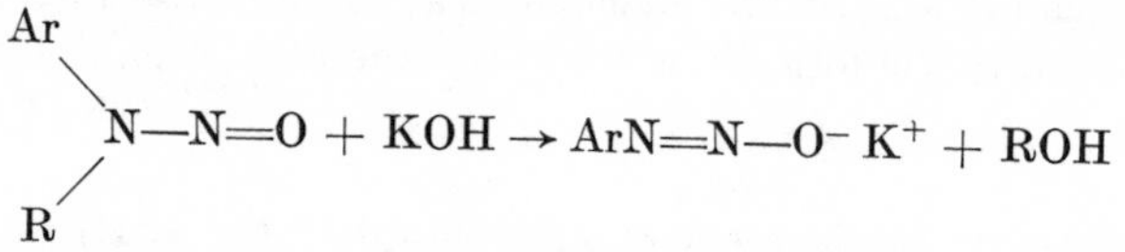

$$\underset{R}{\overset{Ar}{>}}N-N{=}O + KOH \rightarrow ArN{=}N-O^- K^+ + ROH \qquad (7\text{-}2)$$

The pyrolysis of compounds of type III parallels the acetate and xanthate elimination reactions:

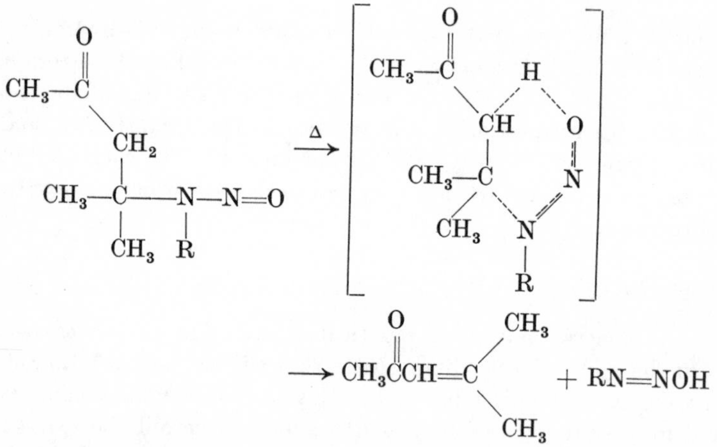

$$\rightarrow CH_3\overset{O}{\overset{\|}{C}}CH{=}C\underset{CH_3}{\overset{CH_3}{<}} + RN{=}NOH \quad (7\text{-}3)$$

The action of dehydrating agents on N-substituted-N-nitrosoglycines gives sydnones (IV). Sydnone imine hydrochlorides are similarly prepared from the nitrose nitrile, with dry hydrogen chloride:

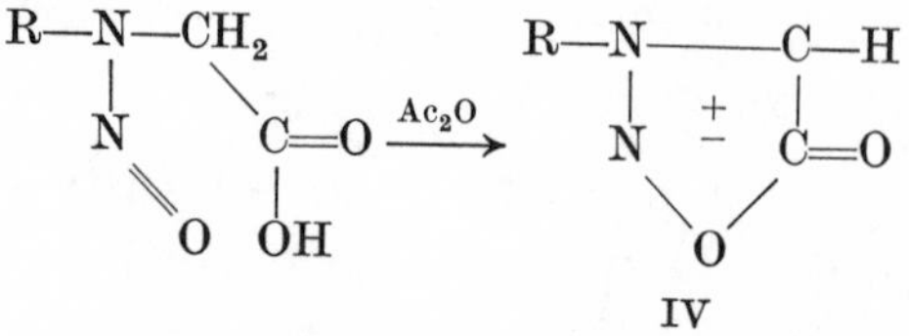

IV

N-Nitroso-N-tosylglycine esters are cleaved to tosylamide, oxalic acid, and hydroxylamine under the influence of bases:[2a]

$$\text{Tos—N—CH}_2\text{COOCH}_3 \xrightarrow{\text{—OR}} \text{Tos—N—CH—COOCH}_3 \longrightarrow \text{TosN} \underset{\text{N}}{\overset{}{\diagdown}} \text{CHCOOCH}_3$$

$$\overset{|}{\text{NO}} \qquad \overset{|}{\underset{\overset{\|}{\text{O}}}{\text{N}}} \qquad \overset{|}{\underset{\text{O}}{}}$$

$$(7\text{-}5)$$

$$\text{TosNH}_2 + \text{HOOCCOOH} + \text{NH}_2\text{OH} \xleftarrow{\text{H}_2\text{O}} \underset{\underset{\diagdown}{\overset{\|}{\text{N}}}}{\text{TosNHC—COOCH}_3} \xleftarrow{\text{H}^+} \text{TosN—CHCOOCH}_3$$

$$\text{OH} \qquad\qquad \overset{|}{\text{NO}}$$

N-Nitrosoacylanilides acylate phenylhydrazine with the formation of aryldiazohydroxide, which reacts further with phenylhydrazine to give benzene and nitrogen:

$$\phi\text{—N—COR} + \phi\text{NHNH}_2 \rightarrow \phi\text{NHNHCOR} + \phi\text{N}\text{=}\text{NOH} \qquad (7\text{-}6)$$
$$\overset{|}{\text{NO}}$$

Grignard reagents add normally to the —N=O bond of N-nitrosamines to give the corresponding hydrazone (7–7a). If the Grignard reagent does not possess an α-hydrogen, a presumed diaziridine (V) is formed, and this is followed by the additive ring opening of another mole of the Grignard reagent (7–7b):

$$\underset{\phi}{\overset{\phi}{\diagdown}}\text{N—N}\text{=}\text{O} + \text{C}_2\text{H}_5\text{MgI} \rightarrow \underset{\phi}{\overset{\phi}{\diagdown}}\text{N—N}\underset{\text{C}_2\text{H}_5}{\overset{\text{OMgI}}{\diagup}} \rightarrow \underset{\phi}{\overset{\phi}{\diagdown}}\text{N—N}\text{=}\text{CHCH}_3 \quad (7\text{-}7a)$$

$$\underset{\text{C}_2\text{H}_5}{\overset{\text{C}_2\text{H}_5}{\diagdown}}\text{N—N}\text{=}\text{O} + \phi\text{MgBr} \rightarrow \underset{\text{C}_2\text{H}_5}{\overset{\text{C}_2\text{H}_5}{\diagdown}}\text{N}\underset{\underset{\overset{|}{\text{CH}_2}}{\text{CH}_3}}{\overset{\phi}{-\!\!\!-}}\text{N} \underset{\text{OMgBr}}{} \rightarrow \left[\underset{\text{C}_2\text{H}_5}{\overset{\text{C}_2\text{H}_5}{\diagdown}}\text{N}\underset{\underset{\overset{|}{\text{CH}}}{\text{CH}_3}}{-\!\!\!-}\text{N—}\phi \right]$$

$$\text{V}$$

$$(7\text{-}7b)$$

$$\downarrow \phi\text{MgBr}$$

$$\underset{\phi\text{—CHCH}_3}{\overset{\text{C}_2\text{H}_5}{\diagdown}}\text{N—NH}\phi$$

The cleavage of N-nitrosamines (denitrosation) to the corresponding amines can be accomplished by several methods. Among the most commonly used reagents are sulfuric and hydrochloric acid, sometimes in combination with stannous chloride, alcohol, zinc dust, or cuprous chloride.

The reaction of nitrosamines with sulfuric acid in the presence of phenol constitutes the Lieberman nitroso test.

Upon pyrolysis, N-nitrosamines decompose via two paths x and/or y, depending on the nature of the substituents.[2b] The products observed are those resulting from the combination of the fragments with each other or their reactions with the solvent:

$$
\underset{R'}{\overset{R}{\diagdown}}N-N{=}O \xrightarrow{\ \Delta\ }
\begin{cases}
\underset{R'}{\overset{R}{\diagdown}}N\cdot + \cdot N{=}O \quad \text{(path x)} \\[2ex]
[R-N{=}N-OR'] \to R\cdot + N_2 + \cdot OR' \quad \text{(path y)}
\end{cases}
$$

(7–8a)

When R is methyl, fragmentation occurs only via y if R' is trityl, while path x is followed if R' is benzhydryl. When R is phenyl and R' is trityl, both x and y are operative.

The photolysis of alkyl nitrosamines in the presence of acids results in the formation of amidoximes. A hydrogen-bonded complex is thought to be the species undergoing cleavage:[2c]

$$
\underset{O}{\overset{\displaystyle R-N-CH_2R'}{\|}} + HX \rightleftharpoons \underset{O\cdots H-X}{\overset{\displaystyle R-N-CH_2R'}{\|}} \xrightarrow{h\nu}
$$

$$
\underset{\underset{H}{\overset{|}{O{=}N^+}}}{\overset{RNH\cdot}{\diagdown}}CHR' \longrightarrow \underset{R'}{\overset{RNH}{\diagdown}}C{=}NOH \quad \text{(7–8b)}
$$

Under the influence of acid, arylnitrosamines undergo the Fischer-Hepp rearrangement. The nitroso groups migrate from the nitrogen to the *para* position of the aromatic ring if the position is open:

$$
\underset{NO}{\overset{|}{\langle \bigcirc \rangle - N - R}} \xrightarrow{H^+} O{=}N-\langle \bigcirc \rangle-NHR \quad \text{(7–9)}
$$

Diphenylnitrosamine reacts with phenylhydrazine with the formation of diphenylamine, aniline, and nitrous oxide:

$$\underset{\phi}{\overset{\phi}{\diagdown}}N\!-\!N\!\!=\!\!O + \phi NHNH_2 \rightarrow \underset{\phi}{\overset{\phi}{\diagdown}}NH + [\phi NHNH\!-\!NO] \rightleftharpoons$$

$$\phi\!-\!\overset{\overset{\textstyle H}{|}}{\underset{\underset{\textstyle H}{|}}{N}}\underset{\diagdown}{\overset{}{}}\underset{\overset{\textstyle N}{\|}}{\overset{}{N}} \rightarrow \phi NH_2 + N_2O \quad (7\text{–}10)$$

$$\overset{\diagdown}{O}$$

Recently[3] an analogous reaction with active methylene compounds has been reported:

$$\underset{\underset{R}{\overset{R}{\diagup}}}{\overset{R}{\diagdown}}\!\!\diagup\!\!CH_2 + \underset{\phi}{\overset{\phi}{\diagdown}}N\!-\!N\!\!=\!\!O \rightarrow \underset{\underset{R}{\overset{R}{\diagup}}}{\overset{R}{\diagdown}}\!\!\diagup\!\!C\!\!=\!\!N\!-\!OH + \underset{\phi}{\overset{\phi}{\diagdown}}NH \quad (7\text{–}11)$$

$$(R = \phi\!-\!, \ Cl\!-\!)$$

N-Nitrosamines may be oxidized to the corresponding N-nitramines.[25b]

The reactions of N-aryl-N-nitrosamines are dependent upon the nature of the substituents on the nitrogen. Aryl-substituted compounds usually cleave to give the aryl radical. Tautomerization to the azo form precedes the decomposition:[4]

$$ArN\!-\!\overset{\overset{\textstyle O}{\|}}{C}\!-\!R \rightarrow ArN\!\!=\!\!N\!-\!O\overset{\overset{\textstyle O}{\|}}{C}R \rightarrow Ar\cdot + N_2 + \cdot O\overset{\overset{\textstyle O}{\|}}{C}\!-\!R \quad (7\text{–}12)$$
$$\underset{N=O}{|}$$

The reaction of N-nitroso alkylamides with base to give diazoalkanes has been described in Chapter 5. White[5] has studied the thermal decomposition of these compounds. It was shown that a diazoalkane is formed in the case where a primary alkyl residue was present. The recombination of the diazoalkane and the acid generated gives the ester (7-13). This method has been suggested as an alternative to the nitrous acid deamination reaction:

$$RCH_2N\!-\!\overset{\overset{\textstyle O}{\|}}{C}\!-\!R' \longrightarrow \left[RCH_2N\!\!=\!\!NO\overset{\overset{\textstyle O}{\|}}{C}R'\right] \longrightarrow$$
$$\underset{N=O}{|}$$

$$R\overset{-}{C}H\overset{+}{N_2} + R'COOH \xrightarrow{-N_2} RCH_2O\overset{\overset{\textstyle O}{\|}}{C}R' \quad (7\text{–}13)$$

When secondary and tertiary alkyl groups are present, it is probable that a carbonium ion is formed; mechanisms operative in the various decompositions have been discussed:[5,6]

$$R_2CHN-\overset{\overset{O}{\|}}{C}-R' \longrightarrow \left[R_2CHN\!=\!\overset{\overset{O}{\|}}{NOC}R'\right] \overset{-N_2}{\longrightarrow}$$
$$\underset{\overset{|}{N}\diagdown_O}{}$$

$$\left[\overset{+}{R_2CH}\quad ^-O\overset{\overset{O}{\|}}{C}R'\right] \longrightarrow R_2CH-O\overset{\overset{O}{\|}}{C}R' \quad (7\text{--}14)$$

The obvious conclusion that emerges from the reactions of N-nitrosamines (I) is that they behave quite differently from C-nitroso compounds (VI) which undergo many coupling reactions in a manner identical with that of aldehydes. This difference between C- and N-nitroso compounds is undoubtedly due to the significant contribution of resonance structure VII, as was shown by spectral studies:

$$\underset{\underset{R'}{\diagup}}{\overset{\overset{R}{\diagdown}}{}}\!N\!-\!N\!=\!\overset{\frown}{O} \longleftrightarrow \underset{\underset{R'}{\diagup}}{\overset{\overset{R}{\diagdown}}{}}\!\overset{+}{N}\!=\!N\!-\!O^- \qquad R_3C\!-\!N\!=\!O$$

$$\quad\quad \text{I} \qquad\qquad\qquad \text{VII} \qquad\qquad\qquad \text{VI}$$

The configuration and conformation of N-nitrosamines has been determined by n.m.r. techniques.[7] Recent results[8] tend to confirm the preference of N-nitrosamines to react at the oxygen atom. These adducts are useful as alkylating agents. With cyclopentadienyl sodium, the corresponding hydrazone is obtained:[8b]

$$\underset{\underset{RCH_2}{\diagup}}{\overset{\overset{RCH_2}{\diagdown}}{}}\!N\!-\!N\!=\!O + R_3'\overset{+}{O}\ X^- \longrightarrow$$

$$\underset{\underset{RCH_2}{\diagup}}{\overset{\overset{RCH_2}{\diagdown}}{}}\!N\!\cdots\!\overset{+}{N}\!\cdots\!O\!-\!R' \overset{\overset{\overset{-}{\bigcirc\!\!\!=}}\ Na^+}{\longrightarrow} \underset{\underset{RCH_2}{\diagup}}{\overset{\overset{RCH_2}{\diagdown}}{}}\!N\!-\!N\!=\!\bigcirc \quad (7\text{--}15a)$$
$$\qquad\qquad X^-$$

Contrary to previous assumptions, tertiary alkylamines react with nitrous acid (at pH 4–5). The cleavage products are an aldehyde, a nitrosamine, and nitrous oxide (7–15b). Some of the postulated intermediates could be isolated when the nitrosations were carried out in anhydrous media using nitrosyl chloride:[2c]

$$(RCH_2)_3N + HON{=}O \xrightarrow[60°-90°]{ag.HOAc} [(RCH_2)_3\overset{+}{N}{-}N{=}O] + H_2O$$

$$\left[\begin{array}{c} RCH_2 \quad N \\ \overset{+}{N} \diagup \quad \diagdown O \\ RCH_2 \quad CH{-}H \\ | \\ R \end{array}\right] \longrightarrow (RCH_2)_2\overset{+}{N}{=}CHR \quad + \quad [NOH]$$

$$\downarrow H_2O \qquad\qquad\qquad 2x \quad (7\text{--}15b)$$

$$(RCH_2)_2NH + RCHO \quad [HON{=}NOH]$$

$$\downarrow HONO \qquad\qquad\qquad\qquad \downarrow$$

$$(RCH_2)_2N{-}N{=}O \qquad\qquad H_2O + N_2O$$

The Overberger-Lombardino Reaction; N-Nitrenes[9]

The reduction of activated secondary N-nitrosamines under basic conditions leads to the elimination of nitrogen and coupling of the resulting fragments:[9b]

$$\phi CH_2{-}N{-}CH_2\phi \rightarrow N_2 + \phi CH_2CH_2\phi \tag{7--16}$$
$$\underset{NO}{|}$$

The similarity of these results[9,10] with those of the oxidation of the corresponding hydrazines (7–17a) suggest that a common intermediate may be involved. Sodium hydrosulfite in the presence of base is the most commonly used reagent, and the reaction has been viewed as going through the following steps:

$$\begin{array}{c} \phi CH_2 \\ \diagdown \\ N{-}N{=}O \xrightarrow{Na_2S_2O_4} \\ \diagup \\ \phi CH_2 \end{array} \qquad \begin{array}{c} \phi CH_2 \\ \diagdown \\ N{-}NHOH \\ \diagup \\ \phi CH_2 \end{array} \;\; OH^-$$

$$\left[\begin{array}{c} \phi CH_2 \\ \diagdown \\ N{-}\overset{\cdot\cdot}{\underset{\cdot\cdot}{N}} \\ \diagup \\ \phi CH_2 \end{array}\right] \quad VIII$$

$$\begin{array}{c} \phi CH_2 \\ \diagdown \\ N{-}NH_2 \xrightarrow{HgO} \\ \diagup \\ \phi CH_2 \end{array} \qquad \begin{array}{c} \phi CH_2 \\ \diagdown \\ N{-}NHHgOH \\ \diagup \\ \phi CH_2 \end{array} \;\; \xrightarrow{-Hg, H_2O}$$

$$\phi CH_2CH_2\phi + N_2 \tag{7--17a}$$

The nature of the intermediate VIII and the mechanism of the decomposition are not certain at present. Several studies have so far not permitted a clearcut decision on the mechanism that is operative. The change in the distribution of products caused by the introduction of substituents on the aromatic residue is too small to have any real significance.[11]   The conditions (heterogeneous) under which both the reduction and the oxidation reactions are carried out do not favor kinetic studies.   If VIII, or a species tending to form VIII, is assumed to be the intermediate, then a three-center type mechanism (7–18) would seem to fit the results better than either a free radical or an ionic mechanism.   This conclusion is based on the fact that the N-nitroso-2,6-diphenylpiperidines and the corresponding hydrazines show greater stereospecificity than the linear compounds under similar conditions.[9,10,12]   Further support for the importance of the three-center type mechanism, at least in the cyclic cases, comes from isolation of 1,2-diphenyl-cyclobutanes from the oxidation of 2,5-diphenyl-N-aminopyrrolidine.[12b] Indeed, if the 1,4-butadiyl radical was involved, as is probably the case in the thermal decomposition of 3,6-diphenyl-1,2-diaza-1-cyclohexene to styrene, then no cyclic hydrocarbon would be expected to be formed:

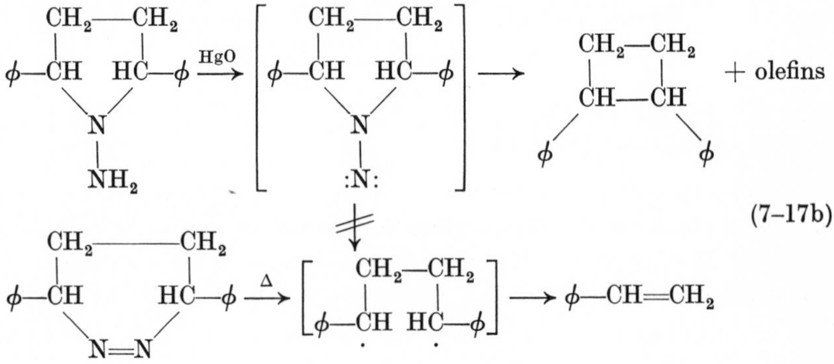

$$(7\text{–}17\text{b})$$

This greater stereospecificity in the cyclic compared to the linear cases would indicate an effect due to the presence of the ring.   In contrast, the thermal decomposition of 3,7-diphenyl-1,2-diaza-1-cycloheptene was completely non-stereospecific:

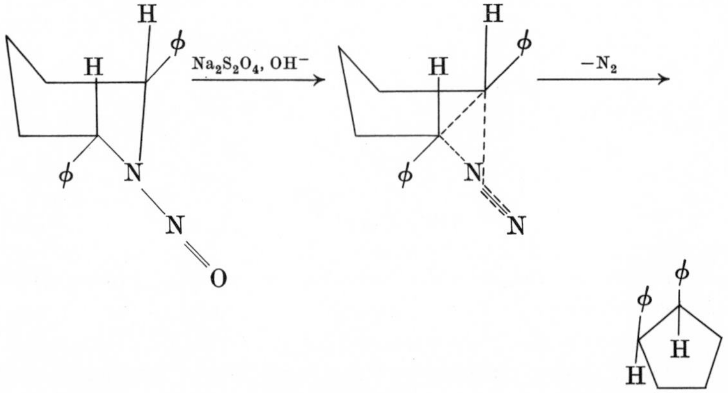

$$(7\text{–}18)$$

This three-center mechanism for the decomposition is presented here only as an improved alternative which in certain cases explains better the formation of coupled products. It does not preclude other mechanisms occurring simultaneously to give other products.

The N-nitrene ($R_2\overset{\cdot\cdot}{N}$—$\overset{\cdot\cdot}{N}$) has become widely accepted as a hypothetical intermediate in a number of reactions, although no concrete evidence for its existence has been obtained as yet. Its only experimental support comes from the work of McBride and Kruse,[13] who presented convincing data in favor of the existence of its conjugated acid (diazenium ion). The existence of C-nitrene (R—$\overset{\cdot\cdot}{N}$) has been demonstrated,[14] and in theory N-nitrene should be even more stable if one considers its similarity with diazoalkanes and azides:

Diazoalkanes:
$$\overset{R}{\underset{R'}{>}}\bar{C}\!-\!\overset{+}{N}\!\!=\!\!N \leftrightarrow \overset{R}{\underset{R'}{>}}C\!\!=\!\!N\!-\!\overset{\cdot\cdot}{N} \leftrightarrow \overset{R}{\underset{R'}{>}}C\!\!=\!\!\overset{+}{N}\!\!=\!\!\bar{N}$$

Azides:
$$R\!-\!\bar{N}\!-\!\overset{+}{N}\!\!=\!\!N \leftrightarrow R\!-\!N\!\!=\!\!N\!-\!\overset{\cdot\cdot}{N} \leftrightarrow R\!-\!N\!\!=\!\!\overset{+}{N}\!\!=\!\!\bar{N}$$

N-Nitrenes:
$$\overset{R}{\underset{R'}{>}}N\!-\!\overset{\cdot\cdot}{N} \leftrightarrow \overset{R}{\underset{R'}{>}}\overset{+}{N}\!\!=\!\!\bar{N}$$

$$\text{A} \qquad\qquad \text{B} \qquad\qquad \text{C}$$

Formally, diazoalkanes and azides can be considered as N-nitrenes (see formulae B). Other indirect evidence comes from the reduction of a presumed N-nitrosimine to the corresponding N-nitrene via a similar reaction;[15] the N-nitrene in this case has been isolated, since it is the corresponding diazoalkane:

$$\overset{Ar}{\underset{Ar}{>}}C\!\!=\!\!N\!-\!N\!\!=\!\!O + LiAlH_4 \longrightarrow \left[\overset{Ar}{\underset{Ar}{>}}C\!\!=\!\!N\!-\!\underset{H}{\overset{|}{N}}OH\right] \xrightarrow[-H_2O]{base}$$

$$\overset{Ar}{\underset{Ar}{>}}C\!\!=\!\!N\!-\!\overset{\cdot\cdot}{N} \qquad (7\text{--}19)$$

As was mentioned previously, the intermediacy of N-nitrenes has been postulated for several other reactions. The N-halohydrazines presumably formed in the bromine and *t*-butyl hypochlorite oxidation of activated 1,1-disubstituted hydrazines[16] lose the elements of hydrogen halide to give the N-nitrenes:

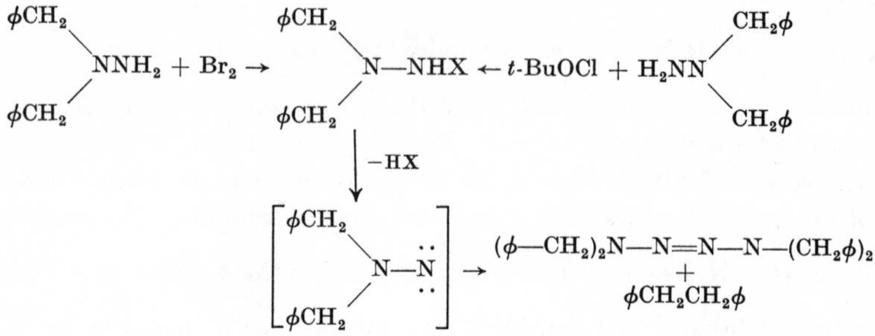

$$(7\text{-}20)$$

The results of the base-catalyzed decomposition of tosylhydrazides reported by Carpino[17a] parallel the elimination reactions of N-nitrosamines and hydrazines. An interesting application of this reaction to the synthesis of alkynes has been reported:[17b]

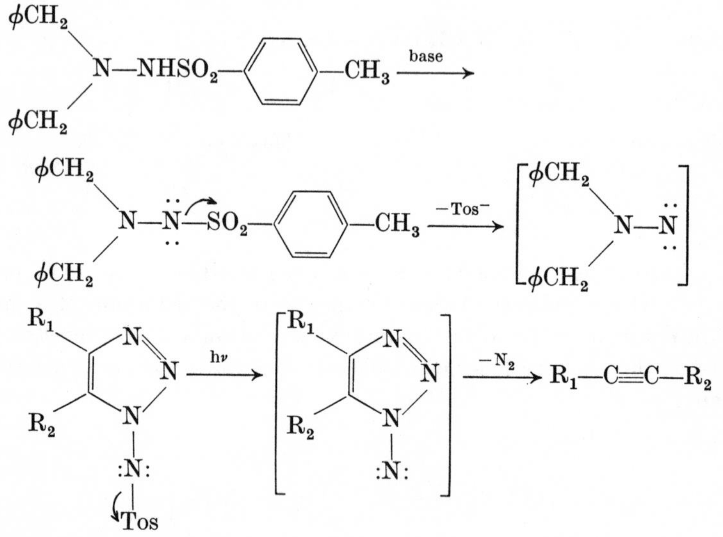

$$(7\text{-}21a)$$

$$(7\text{-}21b)$$

Other reactions that follow the same path include the difluoroamine deamination (7–22),[18] the lead tetraacetate oxidation[19a] of Neber's lactam to 3-cinnolinol (7–23a), the ozonlysis of azomethine (7–23b)[19b] and the conversion of diallylamine to 1-allyl-2-pyrazoline (7.24).[20] This latter reaction is the most pertinent indication to date that indeed such an intermediate N-nitrene is formed:

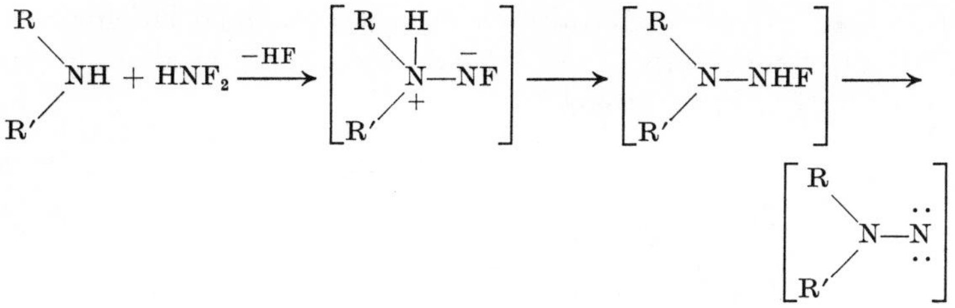

$$(7\text{-}22)$$

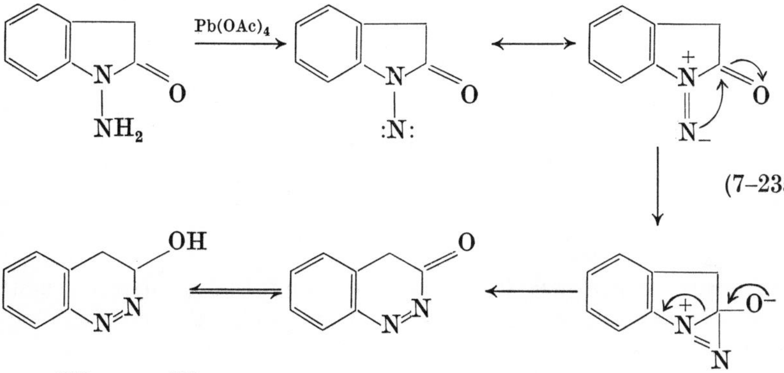

$$(7\text{-}23a)$$

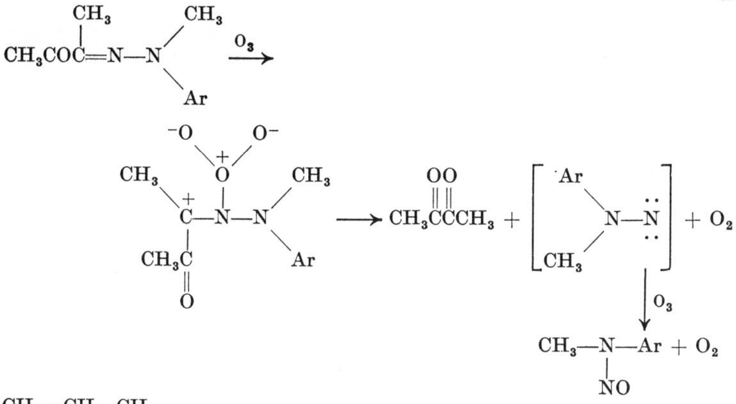

$$(7\text{-}23b)$$

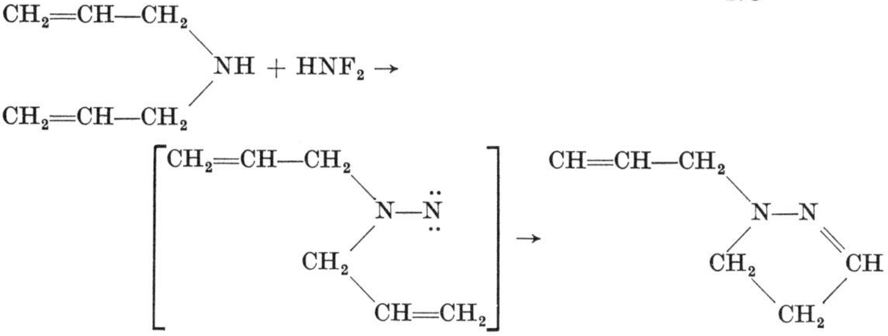

$$(7\text{-}24)$$

In contrast to N-nitroso azetidine[25b], N-nitroso aziridine is rather unstable.[21,25b] It decomposed to nitrous oxide and ethylene on attempted isolation (7–25a). However, its ultraviolet spectrum could be obtained in solution at low temperatures, and it underwent some interesting transformations with Grignard reagents:[21]

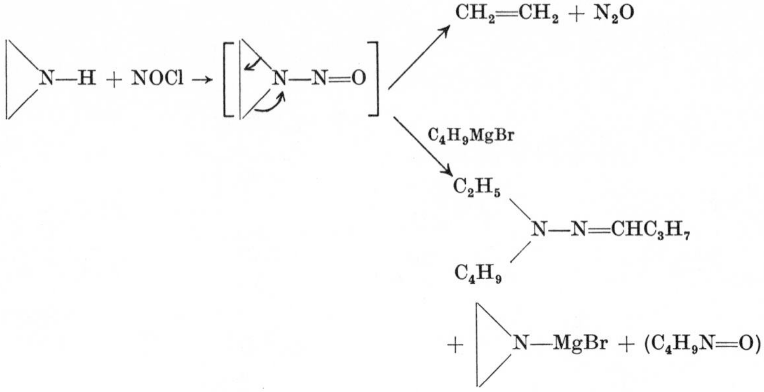

$$CH_2{=}CH_2 + N_2O \qquad (7\text{–}25a)$$

$$\text{N—H} + NOCl \rightarrow \left[\text{N—N{=}O} \right] \nearrow$$

$$\searrow C_4H_9MgBr$$

$$\begin{array}{c} C_2H_5 \\ \backslash \\ \text{N—N{=}CHC}_3H_7 \\ / \\ C_4H_9 \end{array}$$

$$+ \quad \text{N—MgBr} + (C_4H_9N{=}O) \quad (7\text{–}25b)$$

Monoalkyl- and *s*-dialkylhydrazines form N-nitroso derivatives. Dinitroso compounds can lose two moles of nitric oxide to yield the corresponding azo compounds:[25c]

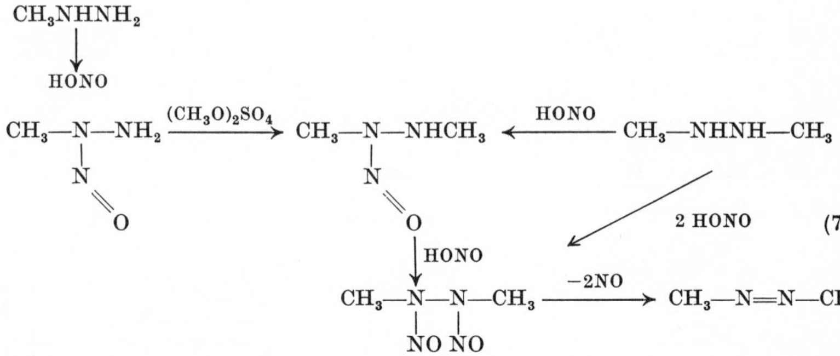

$$CH_3NHNH_2$$

$$\downarrow \text{HONO}$$

$$\underset{\underset{O}{\overset{\|}{N}}}{CH_3\text{—N—NH}_2} \xrightarrow{(CH_3O)_2SO_4} \underset{\underset{O}{\overset{\|}{N}}}{CH_3\text{—N—NHCH}_3} \xleftarrow{\text{HONO}} CH_3\text{—NHNH—CH}_3$$

$$\downarrow \text{HONO} \qquad\qquad \swarrow \text{2 HONO} \qquad (7\text{–}25c)$$

$$\underset{\overset{|}{\underset{\text{NO}}{}}\,\overset{|}{\underset{\text{NO}}{}}}{CH_3\text{—N—N—CH}_3} \xrightarrow{-2NO} CH_3\text{—N{=}N—CH}_3$$

7–4. N-NITRAMINES

N-Nitramines (IX) are structurally related to N-nitrosamines, the nitroso group being replaced by a nitro group:

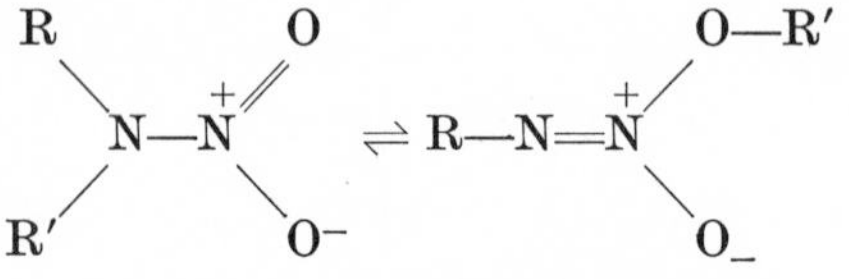

$$\begin{array}{ccc} \underset{R'}{\overset{R}{\diagdown}}\text{N—}\overset{+}{N}\overset{O}{\underset{O^-}{\diagup}} & \rightleftharpoons & R\text{—N{=}}\overset{+}{N}\overset{O\text{—}R'}{\underset{O_-}{\diagup}} \\ IX & & IXa\ (R' = H) \end{array}$$

The chemistry of N-nitramines has not been studied very extensively, and a review by Lamberton[22] summarizes the literature to 1951. Several features of N-nitramines are worth mentioning, especially when contrasted to those of N-nitrosamines. They do not exhibit basic properties and primary nitramines (IXa, $R' = H$) are acidic. Both R and R' in IX can be hydrogen, and this is in marked contrast with nitrosamines. Although the $\diagdown N{-}NO_2$ group is not inherently unstable, explosive properties have been associated with many N-nitro compounds (cyclonite, nitroguanidine, etc.). The structure and the tautomerization of nitramines have been discussed by Lamberton.[22]

Preparation

Owing to the instability of primary nitramines in the presence of acids, indirect methods must be utilized for their preparation. The most common uses an acyl derivative which is nitrated and the primary nitramine released by the action of base:

$$RNH_2 + ClCR_2' \longrightarrow RNHCR' \xrightarrow{HONO_2} RNCR_2' \xrightarrow[2.\,acid]{1.\,base} RNHNO_2$$

$$\overset{O}{\underset{}{\overset{\|}{}}} \qquad \overset{O}{\underset{}{\overset{\|}{}}} \qquad \overset{O}{\underset{NO_2}{\overset{\|}{}}}$$

(7–26)

(R = alkyl)

Other methods for the preparation of primary nitramines involve the addition of diazoalkanes to nitrourethane (7–27), followed by decomposition:

$$R_2'\bar{C}{-}\overset{+}{N}_2 + NO_2NHCO_2C_2H_5 \longrightarrow R_2'\overset{\overset{NO_2}{|}}{CH N}CO_2C_2H_5 \xrightarrow[2.\,acid]{1.\,base}$$

$$R\text{-}CHNHNO_2 \quad (7\text{–}27)$$

Another procedure is the nitration of N,N-dichloroamines in the presence of acetic anhydride, followed by reduction of the resulting N-chloronitramines:

$$RNCl_2 + HONO_2 \xrightarrow{Ac_2O} R{-}\underset{NO_2}{\overset{\,}{N}}{-}Cl \xrightarrow{Na_2S_2O_3} RNHNO_2 \quad (7\text{–}28)$$

Two more recent methods seem applicable equally well to the synthesis of both primary and secondary nitramides:[23,24]

$$R_2\overset{+}{N}H_2\,NO_3^- \xrightarrow{Ac_2O,ZnCl_2} R_2N{-}NO_2 + CH_3COOH \quad (7\text{–}29)$$

$$R_2NH + \overset{CH_3\diagdown \,\,\diagup ONO_2}{\underset{CH_3\diagup \,\,\diagdown CN}{C}} \longrightarrow R_2N{-}NO_2 + CH_3COCH_3 + HCN \quad (7\text{–}30)$$

The nitrolysis of dialkylamides gives the secondary nitramines, although sometimes the nitramides may be formed:

$$R'CO-N\begin{array}{c}R\\ \\ R\end{array} + HONO_2 \xrightarrow[b]{a} \begin{array}{c}R_2N-NO_2 + R'COOH\\ \\ R'CO-N-R + ROH \\ | \\ NO_2\end{array} \qquad (7\text{-}31)$$

Aromatic primary nitramines may be prepared by the oxidation of diazotates. Direct N-nitration of aromatic amines has been achieved recently, using phenyl lithium as base and amyl nitrate as the nitrating agent.[25a] The oxidation of N-nitroso azetidine gave N-nitro azetidine.[25b]

Reactions

Action of Acids. In the presence of acids, primary aliphatic nitramines are decomposed to the corresponding alcohols and nitrous oxide, while aromatic nitramines undergo a Fischer-Hepp type rearrangement. Secondary aliphatic nitramines are not easily affected by acids even at 100°C. The mechanism of the rearrangement of aromatic nitramines has been studied over a number of years,[26] and it has been shown recently that both intramolecular and intermolecular mechanisms are operative.[26e] The action of water alone converts dialkylnitramines to the corresponding hydroxylamines and nitrous oxide. Primary aliphatic nitramines condense with formaldehyde in the presence of acids.[27]

Action of Bases. The elimination of nitrous acid from secondary aliphatic nitramines having α-hydrogens is accelerated by base; the resulting Schiff base is cleaved to the amine and the aldehyde:

$$R-N-CH_2R' \xrightarrow{base, \Delta} R-N{=}CHR' + HONO \qquad (7\text{-}32)$$

$$\begin{array}{c} | \\ N^+ \\ \diagup\diagdown \\ O \qquad O^- \end{array}$$

Most primary aliphatic nitramines are not affected by base, the salt of the compound being formed; these can be added to activated double bonds in a Michael-type reaction.[28]

Miscellaneous. The reduction of nitramines can result in the formation either of cleavage products or of the corresponding hydrazines. O-Substituted primary aliphatic nitramines (which can be prepared by alkylation of the corresponding potassium or silver salts) are decomposed by acids:[29]

$$R-\overset{+}{N}=N\overset{\displaystyle O^-}{\underset{\displaystyle O-R'}{\Big\langle}} \quad \xrightarrow{H^+} \quad ROH + N_2O + R'OH \qquad (7\text{-}33)$$

The pyrolysis of N-nitramides has been investigated and proceeds in a manner similar to that of N-nitrosamides:[30]

$$\underset{\displaystyle R}{\overset{\displaystyle NO_2}{\Big|}}-\underset{}{N}-\overset{\displaystyle O}{\overset{\|}{C}}-R' \rightarrow \left[R-\overset{+}{N}=N-O\overset{\displaystyle O}{\overset{\|}{C}}-R' \right] \rightarrow RO\overset{\displaystyle O}{\overset{\|}{C}}R' + N_2O \qquad (7\text{-}34)$$

REFERENCES

General

F. HITZLER, in J. HOUBEN, *Die Methoden der Organischen Chemie*, vol. 4. G. Thieme Verlag, Leipzig, 1941, p. 90.

A. H. LAMBERTON, Chemistry of nitramines, *Quart. Rev.*, **5**, 75 (1951).

Text

1. (a) M. J. DANZIG, R. F. MARTEL, and S. R. RICCITIELLO, *J. Org. Chem.*, **26**, 3327 (1961).
   (b) T. E. STEVENS, *J. Org. Chem.* **29**, 311 (1964).

2. (a) W. KIRMSE and L. HORNER, *Chem. Ber.*, **89**, 1674 (1956); see also H. U. DAENIKER, *Helv. Chim. Acta*, **47**, 33 (1964).
   (b) W. RICKATSON and T. S. STEVENS, *J. Chem. Soc.*, 3960 (1963).
   (c) E. M. BURGESS and J. M. LAVANISH, *Tetrahedron Letters*, 1221 (1964); Y-L. CHOW, *ibid.*, 2333 (1964).

3. C. H. SCHMIDT, *Angew. Chem.*, **75**, 169 (1963).

4. R. HUISGEN, *Ann.*, **574**, 184 (1951); R. HUISGEN and H. REIMLINGER, *Ann.* **599**, 161 (1956).

5. E. H. WHITE and C. H. AUFDERMARSH, *J. Am. Chem. Soc.*, **83**, 1179 (1961).

6. E. H. WHITE and J. E. STUBER, *J. Am. Chem. Soc.*, **85**, 2168 (1963).

7. G. KARABATSOS and R. A. TALLER, *ibid.*, **86**, 4373 (1964).

8. (a) S. HÜNIG, L. GELDERN, and E. LUCKE, *Angew. Chem.*, **75**, 476 (1963); *Rev. Chim., Acad. Rep. Populaire Roumaine (Romania)*, **7**, 935 (1962); A. SCHMIDPETER, *Tetrahedron Letters*, 1421 (1963); *Chem. Ber.*, **96**, 3275 (1963); D. KLAMAN and W. KOSER, *Angew. Chem.*, **75**, 1104 (1963).
   (b) K. HAFNER and K. WAGNER, *Angew. Chem.*, **75**, 1104 (1963).
   (c) R. N. LOEPPKY, *Dissertation Abstr.*, **24**, 2273 (1963).

9. (a) R. A. ABRAMOVITCH and B. A. DAVIS, *Chem. Rev.*, **64**, 149 (1964).
   (b) C. G. OVERBERGER, J. G. LOMBARDINO, and R. G. HISKEY, *J. Am. Chem. Soc.*, **80**, 3009 (1958).

10. C. G. OVERBERGER, J. G. LOMBARDINO, and R. G. HISKEY, *J. Am. Chem. Soc.*, **79**, 6430 (1957).

11. C. G. OVERBERGER and L. P. HERIN, *J. Org. Chem.*, **27**, 417, 2423 (1962).

12. C. G. OVERBERGER and N. P. MARULLO, *J. Am. Chem. Soc.*, **83**, 1378 (1961); C. G. OVERBERGER, N. P. MARULLO, and R. G. HISKEY, *ibid.*, **83**, 1374 (1961).
    (b) C. G. OVERBERGER and M. VALENTINE, unpublished results.

13. W. R. MCBRIDE and H. W. KRUSE, *J. Am. Chem. Soc.*, **79**, 572 (1957); W. H. URRY, H. W. KRUSE and W. R. MCBRIDE, *ibid.*, **79**, 6568 (1957); W. R. MCBRIDE and E. M. BENS, *ibid.*, **81**, 5546 (1959); W. H. URRY, P. SZECSI, C. IKOKU, and D. W. MOORE, *ibid.*, **86**, 2224 (1964).

14. G. SMOLINSKY, E. WASSERMAN, and W. A. YAGER, *J. Am. Chem. Soc.*, **84**, 3220 (1962).

15. H. E. ZIMMERMAN and D. H. PASKOVICH, *J. Am. Chem. Soc.*, **86**, 2149 (1964).

16. C. G. OVERBERGER and B. S. MARKS, *J. Am. Chem. Soc.*, **77**, 4104 (1955).

17. (a) L. A. CARPINO, *J. Am. Chem. Soc.*, **79**, 4427 (1957); D. M. LEMAL, T. W. RAVE and S. D. McGREGOR, *ibid.*, **85**, 1944 (1963); D. M. LEMAL *et al.*, *ibid.*, **86**, 2395 (1964); **87**, 393 (1965).
    (b) F. G. WILEY, *Angew. Chem.*, **76**, 144 (1964); see also C. D. CAMPBELL and C. W. REES, *Chem. Comm.*, **192** (1965); C. W. REES and R. C. STORR, *ibid.*, 193 (1965). see also ref. 9 of Chapter 2.

18. C. L. BUMGARDNER, K. J. MARTIN, and J. P. FREEMAN, *J. Am. Chem. Soc.*, **85**, 97 (1963).

19. (a) H. E. BAUMGARTEN, P. L. CREGER, and R. L. ZEY, *J. Am. Chem. Soc.*, **82**, 3977 (1960).
    (b) J. P. WIBAUT and J. W. P. BOON, *Helv. Chim. Acta*, **44**, 1171 (1961).

20. C. L. BUMGARDNER and J. P. FREEMAN, *J. Am. Chem. Soc.*, **86**, 2233 (1964).

21. W. RÜNDEL and E. MÜLLER, *Chem. Ber.*, **96**, 2528 (1963).

22. A. H. LAMBERTON, *Quart., Rev.*, **5**, 75 (1951).

23. G. F WRIGHT *et al.*, *Can. J. Res.*, **26B**, 89, 114 (1948).

24. W. D. EMMONS and J. P. FREEMAN, *J. Am. Chem. Soc.*, **77**, 4387 (1955).

25. (a) W. N. WHITE, E. F. WOLFARTH, J. R. KLINK, J. KINDIG, C. HATHAWAY, and D. LAZDINS, *J. Org. Chem.*, **26**, 4124 (1926).
    (b) C. L. BUMGARDNER, K. S. McCALLUM and J. P. FREEMAN, *J. Am. Chem. Soc.*, **83**, 4417 (1961).
    (c) J. THIELE, *Ann.*, **376**, 239 (1910); C. G. OVERBERGER and G. KESSLIN, *J. Org. Chem.*, **27**, 3898 (1962).

26. (a) S. BROWNSTEIN, C. A. BUNTON and E. D. HUGHES, *J. Chem. Soc.*, 4354 (1958).
    (b) B. A. GELLER and L. N. DUBROVA, *J. Gen. Chem. USSR,* **30**, 2627 (1960).
    (c) A. H. LAMBERTON, *J. Chem. Soc.*, 1797 (1961).
    (d) W. N. WHITE, J. R. KLINK, D. LAZDINS, C. HATHAWAY, J. T. GOLDEN and H. S. WHITE, *J. Am. Chem. Soc.*, **83**, 2024 (1961).
    (e) W. N. WHITE and J. T. GOLDEN, *Chem. Ind. (London)*, 138 (1962).

27. L. GOODMAN, *J. Am. Chem. Soc.*, **75**, 3019 (1953).

28. L. W. KISSINGER and M. SCHWARTZ, *J. Org. Chem.*, **23**, 1342 (1958).

29. P. BRUCK and A. H. LAMBERTON, *J. Chem. Soc.*, 3997 (1955); P. BRUCK, J. N. DENTON, and A. H. LAMBERTON, *ibid.*, 921 (1956).

30. E. H. WHITE and D. W. GRISLEY, *J. Am. Chem. Soc.*, **83**, 1911 (1961).

8

Azides and Related Compounds

8–1. INTRODUCTION

Azides (R—N_3) are characterized by the linear arrangement of three nitrogen atoms attached to each other. Covalent structures cannot be written for the azide group; it is best represented as a resonance hybrid of several contributing structures (Ia, b, c):

$$R—\overset{..}{\underset{..}{N}}=N—N \leftrightarrow R—\overset{-}{N}—\overset{+}{N}\equiv N \leftrightarrow R—\overset{+}{N}=N=\overset{-}{N}$$

Ia   Ib   Ic

The R group may be varied from alkyl to aryl and acyl (R'—CO—, RSO_2—, etc.). Several excellent reviews of the synthesis and reactions of azides are available.[1,2,3,4] The discussion will therefore be limited to the essential features and the more recent developments. The synthesis and reactions of acyl azides will be discussed separately.

8–2. PREPARATION

The most common method for the synthesis of alkyl azides consists in the displacement of halo or sulfate groups by metallic or hydrogen azides. Many other groups have been found to undergo displacement:

$$R—X + NaN_3 \rightarrow R—N_3 + NaX \qquad (8–1)$$

The addition of hydrogen azides across an activated double bond is another frequent route to alkyl azides. It is sometimes impossible to introduce the azido function by the two methods above (aryl azides), and a stepwise buildup of the azide is necessary. Several procedures are available.[1]

8–3. REACTIONS

Hydrolysis

The azide group, being a pseudohalogen, can be hydrolyzed under acid conditions to give hydrazoic acid. However, even strong alkali at high

99

temperatures does not attack most azides (but hydrazoic acid may be eliminated with formation of an olefin).   Conjugation of the azido group with activating substituents facilitates the base-catalyzed hydrolysis as in α-azido carbonyl compounds.

Decomposition

As in the hydrolysis, acids catalyze the decomposition of azides, while bases do not, except in special cases.   A whole range of products can be obtained from the acid-catalyzed decomposition of azides.   The reactions have been extensively studied and interpreted.[1,3]   The base-catalyzed decomposition of azido carbonyl compounds presumably involves removal of an α-hydrogen and subsequent formation of the imine:

$$(8\text{-}2)$$

The thermal and the photolytic decompositions of azides have been investigated extensively.   Most often, loss of nitrogen occurs to give electron-deficient species (II) isoelectronic with carbenes, called nitrenes (or azenes or imenes):

$$R\!-\!\overset{..}{\underset{..}{N}}\!-\!\overset{+}{N}\!=\!N \xrightarrow{h\nu\ or\ \Delta} R\!-\!\overset{..}{\underset{..}{N}} \longrightarrow R\!-\!\overset{.}{\underset{.}{N}}\!: \qquad (8\text{-}3)$$

$$\text{IIa} \qquad\qquad \text{IIb}$$

The reactions of nitrenes, which have been shown to have a ground triplet state, have been thoroughly reviewed by Horner and Christmann[5a] and by Abramovitch and Davis,[5b] and will be mentioned only in general terms. (See Eq. 8-4, page 101.)

The first stable "nitrene" has been isolated recently by Smith and co-workers:[5c]

Elimination of hydrogen azide also may take place in some cases:

$$CH_3N_3 \rightarrow CH_2\!: +\ HN_3 \qquad\qquad (8\text{-}5)$$

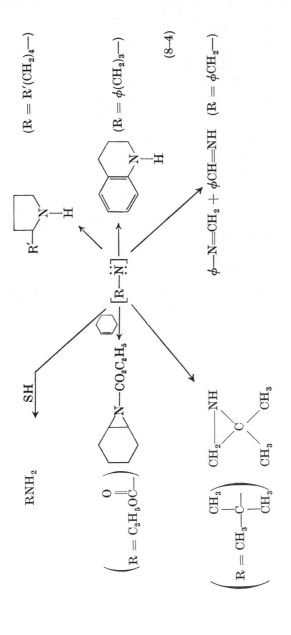

(8-4)

Addition Reactions

Azides undergo numerous addition reactions. The addition of hydrogen proceeds very readily to give the corresponding amines with the expulsion of nitrogen. Both catalytic and chemical methods can be used. This is sometimes the method of choice for the synthesis of amines. Among the compounds that can be added to azides, the reaction of Grignard reagents may be mentioned. The product of the addition of methylmagnesium iodide to phenyl azide, 3-methyl-1-phenyltriazene, is an excellent methylating agent and has the advantage of being stable:[6]

$$\phi\text{---}N_3 + CH_3MgI \longrightarrow \phi\text{---}N=N\text{---}\underset{\underset{CH_3}{|}}{\overset{\overset{MgI}{|}}{N}} \xrightarrow[H_2O]{NH_4Cl} \phi\text{---}N=N\text{---}NHCH_3$$

$$(8\text{--}6)$$

The formation of phosphine imines from azides and phosphine derivatives, first reported by Staudinger and Meyer,[7] presumably involves the generation of a primary adduct:

$$\phi\text{---}N_3 + \phi_3P \longrightarrow [\phi\text{---}N=N\text{---}\overset{-}{N}\text{---}\overset{+}{P}\phi_3] \xrightarrow{-N_2} \phi\overset{-}{N}\text{---}\overset{+}{P}\phi_3 \qquad (8\text{--}7)$$

With unsaturated systems, azides undergo 1,3-dipolar addition. Olefins, acetylenes, nitriles undergo such reactions.[2,8] The reaction of phenylazide with benzaldehyde, recently reported,[9] presumably involved the addition of phenylnitrene ($\phi\text{---}\ddot{N}$) to the carbonyl group to give the ozazirane which oxidized benzaldehyde to benzoic acid:

$$\phi N_3 + \phi CHO \longrightarrow \phi\text{---}N\overset{\overset{O}{\triangle}}{\text{-----}}CH\text{---}\phi \xrightarrow{\phi CHO} \phi COOH + \phi\text{---}N=CH\phi$$

$$(8\text{--}8)$$

Sodium reacts with phenylazide to produce an ion-radical which, if hydrolyzed, gives hydrazobenzene. Further action of sodium on this ion radical yields the disodio salt of aniline:[10]

$$\phi N_3 + Na \longrightarrow \phi\text{---}N\overset{N}{\underset{\underset{Na^+\ -}{\bullet}}{\diagdown}}N \xrightarrow{-N_2} \phi\text{---}\overset{\bullet}{N}:Na^+ \xrightarrow[\ \ \diagdown Na\ \ ]{\overset{\nearrow\ \phi NHNH\phi}{H_2O}} \phi\text{---}N=2\ Na^+$$

$$(8\text{--}9)$$

The reaction of phenylazide with phosphoranes and the lithium salts of benzyl benzenesulfinate and diphenyl benzyl phosphine oxide gives interesting results:[11]

$$\overset{+}{\phi_3 P}-\overset{-}{CHR} + 2\,\phi N_3 \rightarrow \overset{+}{\phi_3 P}-\overset{-}{N}-\phi + \phi N{=}CHR + N_2 \quad (8\text{--}10)$$

$$\phi SO_2\overset{-}{CH}\phi\ Li^+ + \phi N_3 \rightarrow \phi-N{=}CH\phi + \phi SO_2 Li + N_2 \quad (8\text{--}11)$$

$$\underset{\phi}{\overset{O^-}{\underset{|}{\phi_2\overset{+}{P}}}}-\overset{-}{CH}\phi\ Li^+ + \phi N_3 \rightarrow \underset{\phi}{\overset{O^-}{\underset{|}{\phi_2\overset{+}{P}}}}-CH-N{=}N-\overset{-}{N}\ Li^+ \quad (8\text{--}12)$$

Boyer and Morgan[12] have found that alkylazides, under acid catalysis, react with benzaldehyde to give substituted amides:

$$(8\text{--}13)$$

A similar azonium ion is postulated for the reaction of butylazide with carbonium ions, and this intermediate accounts for the products isolated:[13]

$$C_4H_9N_3 + CH_3^+ \rightarrow C_4H_9-\overset{+}{N}-CH_3 \rightarrow C_3H_9-CH{=}N-CH_3 \quad (8\text{--}14)$$
$$\text{and}$$
$$C_4H_9-N{=}CH_2$$

8-4. ACYL AZIDES

Acyl azides are most often prepared by the action of the corresponding acyl halide on sodium azide (method 1). The reaction proceeds readily and in high yields:

$$RCOCl + NaN_3 \rightarrow R\overset{O}{\overset{\|}{C}}-N_3 + NaCl \quad (8\text{--}15)$$

The nitrosation of the acylhydrazides (method 2) is utilized when the ester of the acid is more easily available than the acid, or when the compound is too sensitive to be subjected to the conditions for the preparation of the acid chloride:

$$RCO_2R' + H_2NNH_2 \longrightarrow RCONHNH_2 \overset{HONO}{\longrightarrow} R\overset{O}{\overset{\|}{C}}N_3 + H_2O \quad (8\text{--}16)$$

A recent method[14a] describes the use of "mixed anhydride" which avoids the preparation of the acid chloride (8–17). This procedure gives high yields of the amine, and no isomerization occurs in the case of optically active acids in the Curtius reaction. Furthermore, the acid may be converted directly to the amine without the isolation of the intermediates.   A recent improvement of method 2 utilizes nitrosyl chloride or alkyl nitrites as the nitrosating agents:[14b]

$$RCOOH + ClCOOC_2H_5 \longrightarrow RC\!-\!O\!-\!C\!-\!OC_2H_5 \xrightarrow{NaN_3} RC\!-\!N_3 \quad (8\text{-}17)$$

The main reaction of carboxylic acid azides is their decomposition to isocyanates, known as the Curtius reaction.   This sequence of reactions, critically reviewed by Smith,[3] essentially converts an acid to an amine with one less carbon atom:

$$RCOOH \rightarrow RCOCl \rightarrow ROCN_3 \rightarrow \left[R\!-\!\overset{..}{\underset{O}{C}}\!-\!\overset{..}{N} \right] \rightarrow RN\!=\!C\!=\!O \rightarrow RNH_2$$

$$(8\text{-}18)$$

The intermediate acylnitrene has been trapped as the 1,3-dipolar adduct[15] with benzonitrile and phenylacetylene.   The isocyanate can be isolated or converted to the amine or a derivative thereof (carbamate or urea when the isocyanate is decomposed in the presence of an alcohol or an amine). Sulfonazides do not undergo the Curtius-type reaction under normal conditions.[21]   Acylazides form phosphine imides with phosphines.   Some of the primary adducts (III) have recently been isolated:[16]

$$RSO_2N_3 + \phi_3P \longrightarrow RSO_2\!-\!\overset{-}{N}\!=\!N\!-\!\overset{-}{N}\!-\!\overset{+}{P}\phi_3 \xrightarrow{-N_2} RSO_2\overset{-}{N}\!-\!\overset{+}{P}\phi_3 \quad (8\text{-}19)$$
$$\text{III}$$

Acyl azides are excellent acylating agents.   Aryl halides can be converted in good yields to the corresponding azides[17] by the reaction of the Grignard reagent with a sulfonazide:

$$Ar\!-\!Br \longrightarrow ArMgBr \xrightarrow{RSO_2N_3} ArN_3 + RSO_2MgBr \quad (8\text{-}20)$$

Benzenesulfonazide reacts with anthracene to give 55% yield of 1-benzene-sulfonamido anthracene and only 5–15% each of the 2- and 9-isomers, thus behaving more as a double bond than as a free radical reagent.[18]   An aziridine has been postulated as an intermediate.   Whether or not an acyl nitrene (acyl—N̈) was involved in the reaction was not ascertained:

$$(8\text{-}21)$$

8-5. TETRAZENES AND TRIAZENES

Tetrazenes have four nitrogen atoms and one site of unsaturation. The best-known tetrazenes are the 2-isomers (IV) which can be prepared by the careful oxidation of the corresponding hydrazines and, in certain cases, by the controlled reduction of the N-nitrosamines:

$$
\begin{array}{ccccc}
\text{R} & & \text{R} & & \text{R} & & \text{R} \\
\diagdown & & \diagdown & & \diagdown & & \diagdown \\
\text{N—NH}_2 & \xrightarrow{[O]} & \text{N—N=N—N} & \xleftarrow{[H]} & \text{O=N—N} & & (8\text{-}22) \\
\diagup & & \diagup & & \diagdown & & \diagdown \\
\text{R} & & \text{R} & & \text{R} & & \text{R}
\end{array}
$$

Although a number of 2-tetrazenes are known, their chemistry has not been investigated to any great extent, and little is known about the reactions of these compounds. They decompose upon heating to give the corresponding nitrogen free radicals.[19] The main path of these free radicals is dimerization to the hydrazines, although rearranged products may be formed:

$$
\begin{array}{ccccc}
\text{R} & & \text{R} & \left[\begin{array}{c}\text{R}\end{array}\right] & \text{R} & & \text{R} \\
\diagdown & & \diagdown & \diagdown & \diagdown & & \diagdown \\
\text{N—N=N—N} & \xrightarrow{-N_2} & & \text{N·} & \longrightarrow & \text{N—N} & (8\text{-}23) \\
\diagup & & \diagup & \diagup & \diagup & & \diagup \\
\text{R}' & & \text{R}' & \left[\text{R}'\right] & \text{R}' & & \text{R}'
\end{array}
$$

The reaction with Grignard reagents results in the formation of the amines.[20]

Triazenes (V) are formed by the reaction of amines on diazonium salts (Chapter 5) or by the reaction of azides with Grignard reagents (8-6):

$$\text{ArN}_2^+ \text{ X}^- + \text{RNH}_2 \rightarrow \text{Ar—N=N—NHR} \leftarrow \text{ArN}_3 + \text{RMgX}$$

$$
\begin{array}{c}
\text{V} \\
\Updownarrow \qquad\qquad (8\text{-}24) \\
\text{Ar—NH—N=N—R}
\end{array}
$$

These compounds exist in tautomeric forms and can be cleaved by acids.[6] Reduction with zinc in acid solution gives the corresponding hydrazine and amine. Triazenes can also be alkylated and will explode under rapid heating:

$$\text{ArN}_2^+ \text{ Cl}^- + \text{ArNH}_2\cdot\text{HCl} \xleftarrow[\text{HCl}]{\text{R = aryl}} \text{Ar—N=N—NHR} \xrightarrow[\text{HCl}]{\text{R = alkyl}}$$

$$\text{RCl} + \text{N}_2 + \text{ArNH}_2\cdot\text{HCl} \quad (8\text{-}25)$$

REFERENCES

General

J. H. BOYER and F. C. CANTER, Alkyl and aryl azides, *Chem. Rev.*, **54**, 1 (1954); P. A. S. SMITH, in R. ADAMS, *Organic Reactions*, vol. 3, John Wiley and Sons, Inc., New York, 1946, Chap. 9; E. LIEBER, R. L. MINNIS, and C. N. RAO, Carbamoyl Azides, *Chem. Rev.*, **65**, 377. (1965).

Text

1. (a) J. H. BOYER and F. C. CANTER, *Chem. Rev.*, **54**, 1 (1954).
   (b) N. P. BUU-HOI and P. P. CAGNIANT, in V. GRIGNARD (ed.), *Traité de Chimie Organique*, vol. 15, Masson et Cie, Paris, 1948, p. 715.

2. L. I. SMITH, *Chem. Rev.*, **23**, 193 (1938).

3. P. A. S. SMITH, in R. ADAMS, *Organic Reactions*, vol. 3, John Wiley and Sons, Inc., New York, 1946, Chapter 9.

4. P. A. S. SMITH, in P. DE MAYO, *Molecular Rearrangements*, Vol. 1, Interscience Publishers, Inc., New York, 1963, Chapter 8.

5. (a) L. HORNER and A. CHRISTMANN, *Angew. Chem.*, **75**, 707 (1963).
   (b) R. A. ABRAMOVITCH and B. A. DAVIS, *Chem. Rev.*, **64**, 149 (1964).
   (c) P. A. S. SMITH, L. O. KRBECHEK, and W. RESEMAN, *J. Am. Chem. Soc.*, **86**, 2025 (1964).

6. E. H. WHITE and H. SHEUER, *Tetrahedron Letters*, 758 (1960).

7. H. STAUDINGER and J. MEYER, *Helv. Chim. Acta.* **2**, 635 (1919); H. STAUDINGER and E. HAUSER, *ibid.*, **4**, 861 (1921).

8. R. HUISGEN, *Angew Chem.*, **75**, 604, 741 (1963).

9. L. A. NIEMAN, V. I. MAIMIND, and M. M. SHEKYAKIN, *Bull. Acad. Sci. USSR, Div. Chem. Sci.*, 1498 (1962).

10. T. KAUFFMANN and S. M. HAGE, *Angew. Chem.*, **75**, 248 (1963).

11. H. HOFFMANN, *Chem. Ber.*, **95**, 2563 (1962).

12. J. H. BOYER and L. R. MORGAN, *J. Org. Chem.*, **24**, 561 (1959).

13. W. PRITZKOW and G. POHL, *J. Prakt. Chem.*, **20**, 122 (1963); N. WIBERG and K. H. SCHMID, *Angew. Chem.*, **76**, 381 (1964).

14. (a) J. WEINSTOCK, *J. Org. Chem.*, **26**, 3571 (1961).
    (b) J. HONZL and J. RUDINGER, *Collection Czech. Chem. Commun.*, **26**, 2333 (1961).

15. R. HUISGEN and J-P. ANSELME, *Chem. Ber.*, **98**, 2998 (1965); see also W. LWOWSKI and G. T. TISUE, *J. Am. Chem. Soc.*, **87**, 4022 (1965).

16. J. E. FRANZ and C. OSUCH, *Tetrahedron Letters*, 84 (1963); H. BOCK and W. WEIGRABE, *Angew. Chem.*, **75**, 779 (1963).

17. L. B. BRUNER, *Dissertation Abstr.*, **19**, 438 (1958).

18. J. F. TILNEY-BASSETT, *J. Chem. Soc.*, 2517 (1962).

19. B. G. GOWENLOCK, P. P. JONES, and D. R. SNELLING, *Can. J. Chem.*, **41**, 1911 (1963).

20. R. M. BRIGGS, *Dissertation Abstr.*, **21**, 752 (1960).

21. W. LWOWSKI and E. SCHEIFFELE, *J. Am. Chem. Soc.*, **87**, 4359 (1965).

Author Index

Bibliographic details will be found on pages indicated by italics.

Subject Index